Dolly Westgarth

Dolly Westgarth has written *The Early Caller's Son* around the life of her father, Harry, an inspiring character. Dolly was born into a large family in 1930 and her varied and busy working life started when she was fourteen, working six days a week, ten hours a day in a factory. Forty-eight years and twenty or so different occupations later, she retired from her work as a warden in sheltered housing. She was in amateur dramatics for twenty years, helping to raise thousands of pounds for a local hospice. Now living in Essex, she spends her time writing and teaching art.

THE EARLY CALLER'S SON

Dolly Westgarth

Book Guild Publishing
Sussex, England

First published in Great Britain in 2010 by
The Book Guild Ltd
Pavilion View
19 New Road
Brighton, BN1 1UF

This book is written partly from memory and partly
from stories passed down through the family.

Typeset in Baskerville by Ellipsis Books Ltd, Glasgow

Printed in Great Britain by CPI Antony Rowe

A catalogue record for this book is available from The British Library.

ISBN 978 1 84624 434 6

*I dedicate this book to my father
Harry's memory and to my family*

I would like to thank Maureen Abbot and Muriel and Vic Diss for their help and Jack for his patience

Chapter 1

Harry pressed the crumbly brown earth firmly around the new plants; in a month or so, they should be showing a blaze of colour. As he knelt there beside the small garden he could feel the sun warming his back. Early May was just the right time of year for planting; the weather was still cold but fine and dry. Some of the plots still had daffodils in them but his had been very straggly. Anyway, he liked to get the gardening done as early in the year as possible. There was still a slight chance of frost but it wasn't very likely. When he had finished, he stood up, brushed his hands together and slowly wiped them down the back of his trousers.

'Oh dear, Harry, now you've got dirt on your trousers.' It was Lila; he often heard her when he was working on the garden.

He dusted himself down, stretched out his aching arms, pushed his shoulders back and stifled a yawn. He was so weary!

Harry had been caring for the children for nearly six years now. In the beginning he had managed quite well. Bert's wife Maisie had helped a lot with babysitting and that, but now they were all growing up, and it was more complicated, especially with the girls. What did he know about girls? Lila was the only woman he had been really close to, apart from his mother, of course, and she had always, well, just been there, he hadn't had to understand her. The children were very good

1

about helping around the house, but it wasn't the housework that was getting to him.

Standing there looking down at the new plants, he suddenly felt very angry. 'I need you, Lila; I need you now more than ever. I can cope with the older boys, but the girls and Billy need a mother, and all they have is me.'

Harry suddenly realised that he was speaking aloud. He glanced quickly around but there was no one else about.

'You can do it, Harry.'

Yes, he knew she would say that. 'You can do anything you set your mind to' – that was one of her favourite sayings.

'I can't do it on my own, I can't!' He was doing it again; he really had to stop this habit of talking to himself.

Lila was a good mother; she had raised her children well. The older children always kept an eye on the younger ones and they never seemed to get into trouble like some of their schoolfriends. There were five children. Charlie the eldest was very capable and always so sure of himself. His sister Mary worked hard at trying to keep the house nice. Albert? Well, Albert was a sensitive and kindhearted boy, he had Lila's patience, always looking out for the others and making sure they were all right. Little Rosie, the baby of the family, adored Albert, he always seemed to be there to comfort her if she happened to stumble or needed a cuddle: it was hard to believe he was thirteen now and would soon be looking for work.

Young Billy was different again. He missed his mother even more than the others, if that were possible, he was a very mixed-up young lad, who never seemed to know what it was he wanted. When he was upset or cross about anything he would turn to Rosie. Sometimes Harry would find them sitting on the stairs with their arms around each other, Rosie humming a tune, stroking Billy's wavy hair, Billy, sucking his thumb with his eyes shut tight.

'Rosie is five now and a proper beauty, Lila, she has your brown curly hair and blue eyes and even your smile. The other day she asked me why you had left her. I didn't know what to say.' Blast! He was talking to himself again. Harry could feel the tears stinging the back of his eyes. He wasn't angry any more, just very sad.

'You can do it, Harry.' There was that voice again, that lovely voice, he would never forget the sound of it.

'I can't, Lila, not on my own. What shall I do?'

Did he really think there would be a reply? Some magic solution to his problem perhaps? Well, there wasn't.

He picked up his trowel and the empty plant box and dropped them into his old canvas bag, then, dragging on his jacket and adjusting his cap, he said a sad goodbye to Lila and made his way towards the cemetery gates to begin the long walk home.

Harry was just thirty-five years old. The clothes he wore were neat but well worn. His trousers were shiny, his coat too small and his flat cap frayed around the peak. No amount of spit and polish could hide the fact that his hobnailed boots had seen better days. His bootlaces were just bits of string, blackened with shoe polish. His hair, which had once been dark brown, was now flecked with grey. There had once been a twinkle in those brown eyes of Harry's but since his dear Lila died, it had gone.

The old flower seller was in her usual spot outside the cemetery gates and waved to him. Sometimes on a Sunday when he came to tend Lila's grave he would stop for a chat, but now he just gave a friendly nod and a brief touch of his cap.

A few years ago he would have been walking jauntily along the road, his coat slung over one shoulder, but not today. Today his feet felt like lead as he slowly made his way homeward.

Chapter 2

Harry was born in a small two-up two-down terraced house in the East End of London; he lived there with his mother, father and three brothers. The front door opened straight on to the narrow pavement. His mother Mary was proud of the fact that her doorstep was always clean and white; it never looked dirty, even though she had four lively young sons tearing about. The main reason it stayed so pristine was because the boys and their father were not allowed to set foot on the step. If one of them ever stepped on to their mother's pride and joy, they got a sharp clip around the ear to remind them not to do it again; even Joseph, her husband, sometimes had to dodge out of the way before she clipped him. He would grab her hand and give her a quick kiss. Mary would pretend to be angry, but there was always a twinkle in her eye.

Harry was the third of the four sons. Charlie was the eldest, next was Eddie, then Harry and last of all Sidney. The boys were true comrades as well as brothers; it was them against the world. There was, of course, the occasional scrap between them as with all brothers but it never amounted to anything serious.

Harry's father Joseph worked as an 'Early Caller'. The boys used to call him a 'Knocker Upper': people would pay him to get them up out of bed in the morning in time for work. Mary, his mother, sometimes did sewing for the neighbours, to earn a few coppers.

Food was always in short supply but the family never went really hungry. Clothes were passed down from one boy to the next but they thought nothing of this as it was the same for every other family in the street.

One thing that Harry's family was not short of was love. No one ever actually said the word 'love' but it was all around them. Love was in the food that Mary conjured up out of left-over scraps, and in the well-worn shoes that Joseph mended time and time again. Love was in the way that brother would stand up for brother against anyone who dared to threaten any kind of harm, and yes, even in the way that Mary kept that step so white. Yes, they were short of many things, but love certainly wasn't one of them.

Joseph would sometimes take one or other of the boys out with him on his early caller round. They would be found walking the streets of London before dawn, knocking on doors and windows, waking up men and women in time for work. When Harry went with his father he was allowed to carry the lamp whilst Joseph strode along beside him with the long knocking pole resting on his shoulder. This pole was very important as it enabled Joseph to reach any top-floor windows. He would tap on a window until a face appeared. Some customers were very bad tempered and rude; they shouted and swore at Joseph but he told Harry that you had to expect that sort of thing when you woke people up at the crack of dawn, even if they had asked you to do it. There was a limit, though; Joseph had refused to continue calling up one man who had emptied a chamber pot over him. He wasn't about to put up with that sort of thing.

As each boy turned thirteen his school days ended. Charlie, the eldest, was already working alongside one of his uncles at the docks, whilst Eddie was a 'Carman's Mate', carrying all sorts of goods across London. It was no different for Harry, an uncle had arranged for him to be apprenticed to Joe the coalman.

At last, the day arrived for Harry to start work. He'd been looking forward to it for ages and it had seemed as though the day would never come. Joe took him around the yard and told him that his job would be to shovel the coal into large sacks so that the townsfolk could be supplied with fuel; he also had to chop firewood and tie it up into small bundles. Harry loved the work, he loved everything about it, even the smell of the coal, and especially the fact that he was, as he saw it, doing a 'man's' job.

At the end of the day Harry would stable Joe's horse Ned. He would brush him down and make sure he had fresh hay and plenty of water, all the while talking quietly to Ned, whom he was sure understood every word. Once Ned was settled, Harry would close the stable door and make his way up to the loft above the stable where he slept with two other boys.

During his apprenticeship Harry was not paid a wage but was given bread and tea for breakfast and an evening meal of stewed beef or rabbit. When he had finished his apprenticeship Harry was taken on permanently and allowed to live at home again.

A year later, Sid started an 'Early Caller' round over in East Ham. Joseph was pleased that one of his sons was following in his footsteps.

Working hours were long, free time was in short supply and very precious. Even though Harry loved working for Joe, he made the most of every single minute away from work.

On Sundays in the summer Harry and his brothers would go out to Wanstead Park, a favourite haunt of theirs. The park seemed vast to them, it was green and fresh and very different to the crowded, closed-in streets around their home. There were several lakes in the park and on fine days young people would go swimming and small children would be sailing toy boats made by loving fathers. Others just sat around on the grass enjoying the sunshine and watching the fun. When Harry and his brothers were not swimming they would kick a ball about or lie on the grass flicking bits of twig at one another. Occasionally they would hire one of the rowing boats. They were always larking about. It wasn't unknown for one or other of them to end up fully clothed in the water.

Harry's favourite brother was Charlie: he was full of fun, always laughing and cracking jokes. One year when the lakes froze over Charlie suggested that they all go ice skating. The boys unearthed an old pair of ice skates that had once belonged to their father, and although very rusty, they decided to use them, so they made their way to the park.

There was a lot of arguing about who was going to be first to brave the frozen lake, and as usual it was Charlie who volunteered to go first. The ice looked firm enough but Harry and Sidney were not very happy about the idea of skating on it, and Harry said so.

'It doesn't look very safe to me, Charlie; I'm not going on it.'

'Oh, come on, Harry boy, now we've come all this way it would be a shame not to have a go. It'll be fun. Look, I'll go first if you're worried.'

After a struggle, Charlie managed to fix the skates on to his boots; the straps were very old and worn but he eventually managed to fasten them.

Sidney was standing at the edge of the lake with his hands

in his pockets, looking very worried. 'Last time this lake froze, Charlie, a man got drowned trying to skate on it.'

Charlie laughed, 'What is it with you two? If you're frightened of getting your feet wet me and Eddie will do it. I'll skate across to the other side, Ed, and when I get back you can have a go.' He walked awkwardly across the frost covered grass till he reached a clump of trees; pulling himself out along a thick overhanging branch he launched himself out on to the ice.

Harry and the others stood watching in amazement. Charlie was gliding unsteadily out towards the opposite side of the ice-covered lake with his arms stretched out as if he was going to take flight, and then, all of a sudden, a strap broke on one of the skates. It seemed to Harry as if his brother was swaying there for a very long time, but in fact it was only a few seconds, and then, as if in slow motion Charlie fell. For a whole agonising minute he lay motionless, then, slowly lifting himself up on to one elbow he looked across to where the others were still standing with their mouths open, he laughed out loud, waved, and shouted across to them. 'Ha! See boys, it is thick enough to skate on!' At that, there was an odd creaking sound followed by a loud crack. Charlie's face took on a look of complete surprise as he disappeared through the ice.

Joseph was furious; Harry had never seen his father so angry. When Charlie had been tucked up in a warm bed and Harry and the others had dried off, they were standing, waiting with baited breath for Joseph to punish them. But the boys could not believe their good luck when he said because they had pulled Charlie out of the lake before he was *quite* drowned he would not punish them this time. He thought they had probably learned their lesson already.

The skates were disposed of.

Chapter 3

Harry and his brothers had a lot of fun in their youth as most young men do, but, as the years passed, although they still spent most of their free time in the park, they began to notice the young ladies and were less interested in playing ball or larking about in boats.

On bright Sunday afternoons, groups of young girls would walk along the pathways in the park. They would be decked out in bright cotton dresses and pretty straw hats, and as they walked their curls would bob about their shoulders. The boys would flirt outrageously, at least Charlie and the other boys would, but although Harry tagged along with the others he was always rather quiet and tongue-tied whenever a young lady spoke to him.

One day Charlie brought a young lady home to meet the family and Harry was absolutely smitten; he could not take his eyes off her. She had long brown curly hair and big blue eyes. Her voice was like music to his ears. When she smiled at him his heart would beat so hard and fast against his chest that he thought it would burst out. Even her name had a nice ring to it. He would say it softly to himself when he was alone, 'Lila, Lila.' When he went back to work he secretly told Joe's old horse all about her.

Charlie knew that his young brother was quite taken with his girl, and often pulled his leg about it. Whenever he saw

Harry gazing at Lila, he would draw her attention to it. Lila had a soft spot for Harry and she would tell Charlie not to tease him. Harry got used to Charlie's teasing and would laugh it off. He resigned himself to the fact that Lila was Charlie's girl, and out of his reach.

Eddie was the first of the boys to marry. He married Nancy, the pretty daughter of one of his customers. Charlie and Lila married a year later. Then it was Sidney's turn. Eddie and Sidney and their families moved out to Dagenham in Essex, about twenty miles away. Charlie and Lila moved into a house just a few streets away from the family home. Harry continued living with his parents until they both died. He wanted to stay on in the old house but knew it would be difficult to pay the rent. When he mentioned this to the landlord the man told him not to worry and said that he would sort it out. Later he asked Harry how he would feel if the upstairs was occupied by another family. Harry rather liked the idea, and so it was arranged. So now Harry had a bedroom and a small kitchen, and he was warm and comfortable. Yes, two rooms were quite enough for Harry.

In the dark winter evenings when he arrived home from work, Harry would wash off the dirt and grime from the coal-yard, light his stove, cook himself a meal, and then, more often than not, fall asleep in his comfortable old wooden armchair. When the warmer, lighter evenings came, he was able to sit out in the backyard or on his front doorstep and watch his world, which was the East End of London, pass by. He sometimes carved small toys out of odd pieces of wood for Charlie's children, or the children living in the upstairs rooms. These simple toys gave a lot of pleasure to children who had so little.

Harry would sometimes hear sounds of laughter from the

children in the rooms above him. When he visited Charlie and Lila he loved to be with their children. Perhaps, one day, he would meet a nice girl, one just like Lila, and then, perhaps, he might have a family of his own.

Chapter 4

In 1914 when Britain went to war with Germany men began to sign up for the Army and Harry and his brother Charlie decided to join them. Charlie's wife Lila didn't want them to go; she tried to talk them out of volunteering but they assured her that it would all be over in a few months and said they didn't want to miss out on the action. So off they went to the recruiting office, like a couple of schoolboys again, slapping one another on the back and joking about what a great time they were going to have in the Army.

Unfortunately things didn't turn out quite as they had expected. The recruiting officer turned Harry down flat, saying something about him not being fit enough, and he was really cheesed off about it. 'Not fit? I've been working for Joe, the coalman, for years! I'm fit enough to carry those heavy sacks of coal day after day. Not many men could do that.'

Anyway, Charlie went off to fight for King and country and Harry was left behind.

Harry went round regularly to visit Lila and her little family to make sure that they were all right; he had promised Charlie that he would do this. He patched their worn shoes and fixed the children's broken toys; sometimes he helped Lila with her tiny garden as well. Lila was very fond of her garden. It was only a yard really but in spite of that she managed to grow some very nice vegetables.

One day Harry was having a wash down in his backyard when he heard a frantic hammering and shouting at the front door. He recognised the voice of his young nephew, Albert.

'Uncle Harry! Uncle Harry! Open the door!' It must have been something important because the hammering was getting louder and Albert's voice sounded more urgent. The noise stopped suddenly, and when Harry eventually opened the door he found his young nephew standing there with the old rusty door knocker in his hand. The lad had hammered so hard that the rusty old thing had just given up the ghost and fallen off. Harry knew it had to happen sooner or later. He just hadn't got around to fixing it. He looked down at Albert's small upturned face and saw that it was streaked with tears and dirt. 'What's up, mate?'

'I broke your knocker, uncle.' Albert sniffed and his lips trembled. 'I didn't mean to, honest.' Harry smiled and took the rusty old thing from him.

'Lord luv a duck, Albert, I can soon fix that, there's no need for you to cry about it. What are you doing round here at this time of day? Are you bunking off school?'

Albert lifted his face; his eyes were full of tears. 'They've lost our dad!' He sniffed and dragged a ragged coatsleeve across his wet face. 'Mum's had one o' them telegram things, it says they've lost our Dad!' He sank slowly down on to the doorstep and covered his face with his hands. Harry bent down and, gently lifting the small boy to his feet, took him into the house. After sitting Albert down Harry took a cup down from the dresser and filled it with water. 'Here you are, lad, drink this and you'll feel better.' They sat together quietly and after a few minutes Albert was able to tell Harry all about it. Lila had read the telegram out to the children; it had said that their father was missing in action.

16

What a shocker, Charlie missing! For a moment his mind raced. He ought to do something? But what was there to do, except wait, and hope? He looked down at the tear-streaked face of his young nephew and realised that the boy was expecting some sort of reassurance. He ruffled Albert's hair. 'Don't worry, mate, soldiers often go missing, but they nearly always turn up.' He didn't believe it himself, mind, but it seemed to calm the youngster down. Albert was just five years old, rather quiet and a bit shy. Small for his age, too, not unlike himself really, perhaps that was why he had such a soft spot for the little boy.

Harry had often taken Albert over to the coalyard to see the coalman's old horse. Young Albert loved these visits, he would always have a treat for old Ned, a handful of grass or a piece of apple. After giving the horse these titbits he would take down the brush that was kept hanging by the door, and he would brush that horse until his little arms ached. No amount of grooming would have made old Ned look clean, but young Albert was determined to have a go.

Harry had said to Albert. 'When my boat comes home, Albert, I'll buy you a horse of your own.' Albert must have wondered where the boat was, but there was no doubt in his mind about there being one. Now, Harry pulled on his shirt, took hold of Albert's hand and together they went round to see Lila. As they walked along, Harry held the small boy's hand in his, and every now and again Albert would look up at him for reassurance and he would give the little hand a gentle squeeze.

Harry thought of the day when he and Charlie had gone together to join the Army, how excited they had been, and how disappointed he was when they turned him down. He had been so envious of Charlie, especially when he went to foreign lands, but as the news started to come through telling

17

of how things were going at the front, he was relieved that he was still in dear old Blighty.

Harry could not imagine how awful it was for his brother and those other poor devils serving in France. Gas, mud, sickness and God knows what else. Now Charlie was missing with all that going on. It would be a blessing when the War was over.

Chapter 5

When Harry and Albert reached Lila's house, they found Lila sitting in front of a cold empty grate, looking so small and lost. She wasn't crying, just sitting there saying his name over and over again. 'Charlie, Charlie.' As if by just saying his name she would bring him home.

Harry was standing behind Lila and could see the reflection of her sad face in the mirror over the hearth. He still loved her even after all these years. He wanted to take her in his arms and make the pain go away, but no, it wouldn't have been right. Lila needed Charlie at that moment, not him: he felt very awkward and didn't know exactly what to say to her. He gently laid his hand on Lila's shoulder to comfort her; she turned and looked up at him in surprise. It was almost as if she had expected Charlie to be standing there.

Eventually there were a lot of tears from Lila and the children. It was as much as Harry could do to stop his own tears, so he lit the fire and set young Mary the job of brewing a pot of tea, then he sent Charlie around to the chip shop for five pennyworth of chips and some pies for their tea.

Harry had visited Lila and the family regularly since Charlie had gone away but now his visits became more frequent. She needed to know that someone cared. The other brothers cared, of course they did, but they had families of their own whereas he was single and had only himself to think about.

19

Over the next few months Harry went round to Lila and the family every evening when he finished work; he would clean up first, of course: shovelling coal was a very dirty job.

Lila was very capable and independent and could do most things for herself, but when the evenings came and the younger children were in bed she was glad of Harry's company. It stopped her thinking too much about what was happening to Charlie. She and Harry would sit in the small kitchen and chat over a cup of tea. The older children would be in the front room where there was more space for them to set out their jigsaw puzzles or their drawing paper.

Harry had always felt comfortable with Lila. Even before the children had come along Charlie, Lila and he had spent many an evening together, chatting and laughing over things they had done or seen in their younger days. Lila always had a good sense of fun, but knowing that Charlie was missing somewhere in France, well, there wasn't really a lot to laugh about now.

One day, old Ned (the coalman's horse) snuffed it, and Joe decided that it was time for him to retire as well; he sold up lock, stock and barrel and the coalyard was no more. This meant of course that Harry was out of work. Young Albert was very upset when he heard about Ned. 'Do you think he's gone to heaven, Uncle?' Of course Harry said 'Yes' but really he thought it more likely that the old horse had gone into a few stewpots.

Harry did look for work – he was up every day at the crack of dawn looking for work, but there was none to be had. When the chance of some odd job did occasionally come his way, he would jump at it. He didn't mind what work he did as long as it brought in a few pennies for food. Crikey! Some of the jobs that came his way were a bit 'iffy' to say the least, but he could not afford to ask too many questions. There was one time when he got a job as a bookie's runner; once or twice the coppers were a bit too close for comfort. He had chucked that job in sharpish. The last thing Harry wanted was to get pinched. Where would Lila and the children be then?

Chapter 6

One day the letter came to inform Lila that Charlie had been declared 'officially dead'. They had expected it, really, but seeing it in black and white brought it home. Harry couldn't read but he and the children gathered around Lila and she read the letter to them. The children didn't say very much. Charlie, the eldest boy, went off into a corner of the yard by himself. Mary put her arms around her mother and young Billy and they wept quietly together. Harry felt that he was in the way and had decided to go for a pint of ale but as he was about to leave the house he found young Albert sitting on the stairs sobbing his little heart out. He sat down beside him and they comforted each other.

Just a few months later the fighting stopped and there was peace at last. Lila had been pregnant with Billy when Charlie went into the Army, so he had never seen his son and now Billy would never see his father. It was such bad luck for Charlie to lose his life, so near to the end of the war, too.

After a while Harry moved in with Lila and the family. He slept in the boys' room, it was a bit cramped with the four of them in one room but it was miles better than living on his own. He had grown very fond of Charlie's family; in fact, as time passed he began to feel as if they were his own.

One day Harry and Lila were sitting quietly in the cosy little kitchen, she was busy sewing and he was carefully painting a small fort he was making for Billy. He paused in his work and looked across at her; it seemed to him that she had hardly changed since the days when she and Charlie were courting. Lila suddenly looked up from her sewing and saw him gazing at her. 'What is it, Harry, is something wrong?' Harry realised that he had been holding his breath; he exhaled and took a breath before saying, 'Marry me Lila.' He wasn't really surprised at her answer but he was disappointed. 'Harry, I'm sorry, duck, but I really don't think I can, it just wouldn't feel right. Please don't be too hurt. You have been so kind to us, especially since Charlie went away.'

One evening, a few months later when the children were in bed, Harry and Lila were again relaxing in the kitchen. Lila turned to him and said, 'Harry, do you think it would be wrong if I were to marry you? I mean, is it disloyal to Charlie's memory?'

'Of course not, duck, I feel sure he would be pleased for us to marry. You know before our Charlie went away he made me promise to look out for you all.'

Harry saw the tears come into her eyes. He went to her and put his arms around her. 'Please don't cry, duck, I didn't mean to upset you. I love you, Lila, have done ever since the day you came through the door with our Charlie. I wanted to take you away and run off with you.'

Lila told Harry that she had been afraid he was asking her to marry him out of pity. Harry laughed and she laughed with him. They hugged and kissed each other and danced around the small kitchen.

'Can I take that as a yes then?'

'Yes! yes! yes!'

The wedding was a quiet affair. Lila and her sisters-in-law had managed to get enough food together for a wedding breakfast and after the ceremony everyone squeezed into Lila's front room to eat. When the meal was over the men went off to the pub for a pint or two, the women had a good old chinwag over the washing-up and the children played 'Ring'o'roses' and 'Blind man's bluff'. When the washing up was done the mothers joined the children in the party games and there was a lot of laughter and falling about. They had just finished a very noisy round of 'Here we come gathering nuts in May', when the men arrived home and it was time to say a fond goodbye. All the guests left for their own homes, leaving Harry and Lila and their children to spend a happy evening getting used to the new situation. At last Harry had a family of his own.

Chapter 7

The war had been over for some time. 'Our side' were supposed to have won the war but when Harry saw all those poor bedraggled wounded men coming home, he did wonder what the other side looked like. He was still out of work and life was hard, but things seemed to be going along fairly well for them. He managed to earn a few bob here and there. Lila was a good cook and could make a meal for the whole family out of practically nothing; Harry didn't know how she did it. She would buy a scrag end of mutton or half a rabbit and with a few vegetables from her garden would conjure up a mouth-watering stew topped up with delicious fluffy suet dumplings. The smell and taste of Lila's stew was so good that the family always reckoned it was fit for a king. Harry and the children were getting along really well, why wouldn't they? They had always had great fun when he was their uncle, the only difference now was that he was their stepfather as well.

One day the word went around that the sugar factory was taking on men. Harry could not get out of the house quick enough; as he ran, it seemed as if he was followed by a shower of meteorites: it was the sparks from the metal studs in his boots as they struck the cobbles. When he reached the factory, the place was swarming with folk looking for work. There must have been fifty or sixty men and women, all shouting and pushing, trying to get near so as to be noticed by the foreman.

Harry managed to squeeze his way through the crowd to the front; he even clambered up on to one of the factory gates.

The noise was deafening, people were waving newspapers, scarves, caps, and in fact anything they had, trying to attract the foreman's attention. They shouted at the tops of their voices, 'Here, guv, I'm your man!' 'Give us a break, guv' or 'Take me on, guv, I'm a good worker'. Harry shouted as loud as the rest, he waved his cap about too. Suddenly his foot slipped and he almost lost his grip on the great iron gate. The movement caught the foreman's eye: he pointed to Harry and called out, 'Come on, Nobby, get inside before you kill yourself!' Harry couldn't get down from that gate quick enough, he said a silent prayer of thanks – he was going to be employed at last. He was so excited that he felt like jumping for joy, he could almost have hugged that foreman. A few others were called in along with Harry but many poor devils were left standing outside the gate. These folk still had to find a way to feed their families for another day without work.

Things began to look up for Harry, Lila and the family. He was working, the children had good shoes on their feet and there was always enough food to put on the table. Lila bought some pretty material and made new dresses for herself and Mary, the boys all had new shirts and Harry even bought himself a new titfer tat (hat).

Chapter 8

It was decided that to celebrate Harry's good fortune they would take the family out on a trip on the Woolwich Ferry. Everyone was excited and could hardly wait for the day to come, but come it did. The ferry terminal was only a penny tram ride away and the ferry ride itself would be free. It was the closest they were likely to get to any kind of holiday.

Lila packed up cheese and pickle sandwiches and put some cold sweet tea in a bottle. The children were very excited; they kept telling Lila to hurry up and were in and out of the front door more times than she could count, then, at the last minute Harry lost his cap. Harry always seemed to be losing his cap. A full scale hunt took place. Hunting Harry's cap was always part of the fun of going out for the children; in fact it was usually one of them who had hidden it, it was all in good fun though. The precious cap was of course eventually unearthed and they set off for the Woolwich Ferry.

First there was all the excitement of riding on the tram. There was a short walk before they reached the tramline. The line ran along the middle of the road. When the tram came clanging along, it was all bright paint and gleaming brass handrails, the children could hardly contain their excitement. They clambered aboard and whilst the children clattered up the open stairway to the upper deck, Lila and Harry found a seat inside. The seats were just made up of bare wooden slats

29

and were not at all comfortable but they were all too excited to care much about such a minor detail.

The tram reached the ferry terminal, all the passengers alighted, and Harry, Lila and the children stood at the side of the road and watched the driver and conductor getting the tram ready for the return journey. They pulled a long pole from underneath the tram, hooked it on to the big arm that reached up to the electricity cable, disconnected it, then, swinging it round to the other end of the tram, connected it up again and off they went back along the line, all shiny and bright. The children were fascinated; Billy wanted to go back on the tram, but Harry reminded him that the ferry was waiting.

As soon as the tram was out of sight they hurried down towards the ferry terminal. Everyone clambered aboard and made their way to the main deck with all the other foot passengers. People with bicycles, motorbikes or cars had to go up the slope and on to the top deck. It took quite a long time to get everyone on board but as soon as it was done the gangplank was raised.

Harry and the children made their way down to the engine room; this had always been Harry's favourite place on the ferry. There was an enormous window and through it people could watch the engine working with its great shiny brass pistons thrusting backwards and forwards, slowly at first, then gathering speed as the ferry left the terminal. That massive engine shone like gold, it was fascinating to see it working. Two men were oiling the joints to keep them in good order; the men worked very hard to keep those engines looking so good. The faces of the youngsters looking through the window shone almost as brightly as the engines. The noise, the heat and the smell of oil filled the children with excitement and as they watched the engines working, they breathed in the atmosphere and imagined they were sailing far away to foreign lands, instead of just chugging across the River Thames.

Lila meanwhile was sitting up on deck; for a while she watched the barges going by, but then, feeling the warm sun on her face and the cool breeze in her hair, she closed her eyes. She listened to the rhythm of the engine coming from below, enjoying the fact that for a short while she had absolutely nothing to do, except savour the moment.

When Harry managed to drag the children away from the engine, they joined Lila on deck where they sat and ate their cheese sandwiches. It took about half an hour to cross the river on the ferry but to Harry, Lila and the children it was a trip to remember.

When the ferry reached the other side all the passengers disembarked. In the happy jostling crowd it was difficult for Harry and the family to keep together; however, they did eventually find each other and made their way to the nearest public house to quench their thirst. They sat outside in the sunshine on wooden benches, Harry and Lila each enjoying a half pint of light ale and the children gnawing away at large arrowroot biscuits which they washed down with the sweet refreshing cold tea they had brought with them. The children were all talking excitedly about the ferry ride. Charlie said, 'One day, I'm going on a big ship and I'll sail right across to the other side of the world.' Mary scoffed, 'Don't be silly,' she said, 'You have to be rich to do that, you will never have enough money.'

'I will if I save up, when I start work I'm going to save all my money and then I'll go on a great big liner, I will won't I, Dad?'

Harry chuckled. 'I'll tell you what Charlie boy, when my boat comes home we'll all go.'

Harry told the children there was another way back, underneath the river, they could hardly believe it and begged to be taken back that way. Billy was very worried. 'It's alright for all of you but I can't swim.' Harry laughed and explained that there was an underground tunnel to walk through, and it was very dry.

They decided to go back under the river.

When they were refreshed and rested they made their way to a round building that looked rather like a large sentry box. It housed the big lift that would take them down to the underground tunnel. Some people were already waiting, the family joined them and when the lift eventually came up they all piled into it. The lift was like a big cage and when everyone was safely aboard the attendant heaved the huge iron trellis gate shut with a loud clang, he pressed a button, and the big old lift juddered its way noisily and very slowly back down to the bottom of the shaft. As the lift rattled its way down, the children noticed that people could be seen outside the lift cage; Harry explained that these people had decided to use the stairs. The iron stairway wound its way around the lift shaft and as people hurried down; their echoing footsteps could even be heard above the rattle of the lift and sounded more like an army than a small group of people.

The lift finally reached the bottom and as soon as the attendant opened the iron gate everyone spilled out into the tunnel to start the long trek to the other side of the river. Billy was so excited, he spent his time running on ahead of the family, then tearing back again. He had done the journey twice over by the time they reached the other end. The whole tunnel echoed with the sound of children's voices, it was very exciting, and more than a bit frightening to think of all that water flowing above them in the River Thames.

The long walk tired them all out and the tram ride home rounded the day off nicely. Harry looked at the happy faces of the three eldest children and the contentment on the face of the sleeping Billy. He could feel the warmth of Lila's body as she sat close to him and he thought life was very good indeed.

Chapter 9

One day Harry was at work and the foreman sent for him. 'Nobby, mate, your old neighbour called in to say that you've got some trouble at home, you had better get off straight away.' Harry wondered what sort of trouble but the foreman didn't know.

Harry positively flew home; he had never peddled that bike so fast, and made the journey in half the usual time. He arrived home to find Mary waiting for him at the front gate, her eyes red from crying. The words came out so fast that Harry could only understand half of what she was saying and just managed to make out that Lila had been taken ill and was in bed. He threw down his bike and dashed into the house. He sent Mary to make a pot of tea to give her something else to think about. Climbing the stairs three at a time he dashed into the bedroom and found Lila in a terrible state. Her face was as white as a sheet and he could see blood on the bed. Mary, poor child, had found her mother like that when she arrived home from school: no wonder she was upset.

'What's the matter, duck, what has happened?' Lila turned and saw the worried look on his face. Her eyes were glistening, and as she spoke the tears spilled over, 'Oh! Harry, I'm so sorry, I'm so sorry!' Harry put his arms around her and they clung together. She had had a miscarriage.

Mary was a great help, she was only nine years old but was

not afraid of hard work, very like her mother in that respect. She stayed home from school a lot at that time because Lila was quite ill. The School Board Inspector called round several times to see why she was not attending lessons but he was a very understanding man and there was never any real bother about it.

Lila was very weak for a long time but she slowly recovered, much to the relief of the family and life returned to some sort of normality.

Chapter 10

There was another visit from the School Board Inspector a few months later. It seemed that Charlie had started playing truant. Harry and Lila could not understand it; he always seemed to enjoy his time at school. For a boy his age he was usually quite well behaved. He had been scrumping apples on a few occasions but most boys got up to that at some time. Lila had made some very tasty pies with those apples. Harry supposed he was just a normal twelve year old trying to find his feet.

Young Charlie was ruddy cheeked and well built, he had a mop of unruly sandy coloured hair, he was the image of his father, and whenever Harry looked at him he was reminded of his brother. The lad had also been blessed with Charlie's sense of fun.

One day, a chap at the factory told Harry that he had seen young Charlie working on the barges down on the river. He tackled him about it but Charlie denied it, so one day Harry went down to the docks and caught the young blighter at it. Lila wanted Harry to give the boy a 'taste of his belt' but he couldn't do it. After all, he wasn't the boy's father, and anyway, Charlie was bigger than him even though he was only twelve, so Harry just gave him a good talking to. Later, they went down to the docks together and Harry arranged for him to work there at weekends until he left school.

Charlie told Harry he was trying to earn enough money to buy a bicycle. 'Sorry, Dad, I couldn't expect you to buy me one, could I? Not with all of us to look after.' Harry was fond of Charlie and this little episode seemed to bring them even closer.

Lila's health slowly improved, though she never did get back to her old self and seemed to have lost that spark she used to have.

Harry decided to take the family out for some fun and thought a variety show would be just the thing. They went to the East Ham Palace and saw wonderful Nelly Wallis; she sang their kind of song. As they walked home they were all laughing and talking about the show. Harry had always enjoyed a good old sing-song; sometimes he entertained the men at the factory during the lunch breaks. Lila seemed a lot brighter after seeing the show; in fact, it cheered the whole family up so much that Harry promised to take them again as soon as he could afford it.

A few months later Harry was as good as his word and once again they made their way to the Palace. This time they saw Max Miller and they all said he was the funniest man they had ever seen. His suit looked as if it had been made from his mother's curtains. Harry and the children laughed all the way through his performance. Max Miller's jokes were a bit near the knuckle. Lila said she thought he was very rude but Harry noticed that even she was laughing behind her hand. It was all good clean fun and as the audience left the theatre many of them were singing the old music-hall songs.

Next day people would be humming or whistling those same tunes on their way to work. Harry could always remember every word but he still couldn't read; he felt bad about that, he had always had a good memory, though, and in a way that made up for not reading. Lila used to read the newspaper out to him so he didn't feel as if he was missing out on anything.

Yes, Harry had a nice little family, a comfortable home, a job he enjoyed and a lovely wife whom he loved and who loved him. He was a very happy, contented man.

Chapter 11

'Harry! Did you hear me?'

'What? What did you say, duck?' Harry was dozing and hadn't heard a word. They had been chatting about their day and Lila was telling him what the children had been doing and her soft voice had lulled him off to sleep. She laughed now. 'You didn't hear a word, Harry, now admit it!'

'No, sorry, duck, what were you saying?'

'I said, I'm pregnant.'

Harry was wide awake now, but when he didn't comment, Lila wondered why.

'You don't mind, do you, Harry?'

'No, no, of course not, but how do you feel about it? Remember when you lost the baby, the doctor said it would be best if you didn't have any more children.'

'Oh, Harry, that was ages ago, I'm fine now. There's nothing to worry about, everything will be all right this time, you'll see.'

He nodded, 'Mmm.' He was worried, of course he was, but he didn't want Lila to know it. They were in the kitchen. He was sitting in the big wooden armchair that had once belonged to his father, now it was his and he was very attached to it. Lila always gave it an extra buff-up when she was polishing. The chair was the only piece of furniture he had brought with him from his old home. Lila put down her sewing and pulled her chair closer to his. She touched his arm and said. 'What's the matter, duck, you haven't said much. Aren't you pleased about the baby?'

He turned and laid his hand on hers. How small and fragile her hand felt under his.

'It's not that, duck,' he said. 'Of course it will be wonderful to have a kiddie that's yours and mine, but after the miscarriage you were so ill. Perhaps it's not the best thing for you just now.' Lila smiled up at him and planted a kiss on his cheek.

'Oh, Harry, don't worry about that. I'm stronger now, everything will be all right, you'll see.'

As time went on Lila was very happy about her pregnancy. It seemed to Harry that she was always knitting and sewing. He often came in from work and found her sitting in his big armchair with some small half-finished baby garment, all the while humming away to herself. She seemed well enough, but got tired very quickly; when he mentioned this to Lila she said it was natural for pregnant women to get tired.

When the time came for the baby to arrive, the doctor said it would be best if Lila went into hospital for a while, just for a rest. When Lila's baby was born everything seemed all right, at first anyway. The children were thrilled to have a new baby sister. She was beautiful, and good as gold. When she was just a few weeks old she was taken to the parish church to be christened. Lila decided that her name would be Roseanna, but when the service was over and even before the little family party reached the house everyone was calling her Rosie.

As the weeks went by, although Rosie flourished, Lila's health went downhill. She would sit and watch the baby being fed by Harry or one of the children; she didn't even have the energy to hold the little mite. One evening Harry laid the baby in Lila's arms and watched as she held the tiny hand. She gazed at the baby in her arms and the tears began to roll down her face.

'Harry, she's beautiful, isn't she?'

'Yes, she is, just like her mother.'

He was sitting close to her, supporting the baby's head. Lila laid her head on his shoulder and smiled through her tears. 'Harry, take care of her, won't you, and tell her about me when she grows up?'

'Don't say that, duck, I won't need to tell her about you, she will find out for herself, she will be with you all the time whilst she's growing up.'

Lila bent and kissed the little head.

'Put her to bed now, Harry. It's very late and time she was asleep.'

He took Rosie up and tucked her into her cot. When he went back down to join Lila, he found her fast asleep. He covered her with a blanket and sat looking at her for some time; he didn't want to disturb her. She was very pale; she hadn't been eating properly since Rosie was born.

Lila's health deteriorated even more and it broke Harry's heart to see her getting so thin and pale. Then, the dreadful day came when the doctor said he wanted her to go into hospital again. He told Harry there was very little hope.

Lila was taken into hospital, and never came out again. She just faded away.

Chapter 12

After the funeral the house seemed dead. Mary and the boys looked after little Rosie between them; she was a beautiful little thing, soft brown curls just like her mother's, and the same big blue eyes too.

Rosie was always happy in those early days. She hadn't known any different life, had she? She didn't miss her mother because she hadn't known her. The older boys were marvellous with her, they idolised her. Little Billy was a bit put out for a while. He missed his mother terribly. They all did, of course, but Billy being the youngest before Rosie came along, felt it more than the others. He had a few bad tantrums at first and hadn't wanted anything to do with the baby. Rosie was a proper charmer though and it wasn't long before Billy was spoiling her, just like the others.

Harry loved Rosie, too, of course he did. She was his and Lila's child, but sometimes he would look at her and think, 'If only,' then Rosie would come up and throw her arms around him. And that was that.

Charlie started work full time and was bringing in some money, which made things easier. It meant that they were even able to afford their favourite meal of saveloys and pease pudding from the high-street shop. This pleased Mary, it meant that she didn't have to cook. Everyone liked those spicy red sausages and golden pease pudding. Each of the children looked forward to when it would be their turn to fetch the meal because then they were allowed to buy themselves a pennyworth of chips to eat on the way home.

After a while the family's life settled into some sort of order.

Little Rosie desperately wanted a mother. Harry had come home from work one day to find her in tears. He lifted her on to his lap to comfort her.

'What is the matter, duck, why all the tears?'

She looked up at him with those big blue eyes of hers and said, 'Daddy, why haven't I got a Mummy?' He was quite taken aback by this; she had never asked that question before, why now?

'Well, you've got me, duck, and Mary and the boys and we all love you. You're happy, aren't you?'

'Yes,' she, said. 'But all the other children have got a Mummy. Why haven't I?' He told her how when she was a tiny baby Lila had cuddled her and had loved her very much. They looked at the painting of Lila and he told her that she was just like Lila. Little Rosie cried even more, saying, 'Well, if she loved me why did she go away and leave me?'

Later that same evening when the family were in bed Harry sat up alone, gazing into the empty grate. What they needed was a housekeeper, a kindly woman to care for Rosie and the others. It was stupid of him to think he could be both father and mother to them; perhaps he was too rough for the job. Yes, what they needed was someone like his friend Wally's missus, just that sort of motherly person. Someone who could give them more time than he could. His mind made up, Harry went to bed satisfied that he had made the right decision.

Harry decided to advertise for a housekeeper and went round to speak to Wally's wife, Maisie. She would know more about what to write to attract the kind of person that he needed to care for his family, and of course she would write the card out for him.

Maisie was pleased to help and soon he was on the way home with the card in his pocket. He wanted to tell the children about his decision before he put the card in the shop window. When he explained to the children that they really couldn't manage on their own any more, Mary made a proper fuss.

'Uncle Harry, if you bring some old bag into this house to boss us around, I'm leaving.' She was nearly sixteen now and had a mind of her own. Mary had been the woman of the house for a long time and had made a good job of it. She was a good cook, and managed to keep the house tidy. Although, having three boisterous boys in and out all the time didn't help much. She nagged them but it didn't make a bit of difference. The boys were all right about having a housekeeper; they didn't really care one way or the other so long as they were fed.

Harry was more worried about Rosie; she was only five years old and needed a woman to care for her. Mary had always taken care of Rosie, but he sometimes thought she secretly blamed the little girl for the death of her mother. Oh, she had never said as much, but Harry somehow knew that it was how she felt. He decided to go ahead with his idea of getting a housekeeper and he promised Mary that she would have a say in who was taken on.

Chapter 13

Two weeks later Harry was on his way home from the cemetery when it began to rain quite hard. Little streams of water
were running off the peak of his cap and he could feel the
wet rain seeping through his thin coat. The bright lights of
the public house caught his eye and he was drawn towards
them knowing that inside he would find a room that was warm
and dry.

Harry pushed the heavy door and it opened into a bright,
noisy bar. The air was heavy with smoke and the sweet smell
of beer was all around. Groups of men were standing about
drinking, smoking, talking and laughing together, some were
standing around the dartboard where there was a game going
on. Around the room were long wooden benches with soft
padded leather seats, with a wooden table set in front of each
bench. The tables held an assortment of drinks and biscuits
belonging to the womenfolk. The women too were busy chatting occasionally sipping their drinks or nibbling at their biscuits.

Harry glanced around the large room full of happy people.
He wasn't really in the mood for company, but he needed to
get out of the rain for a while. As he stepped inside some
heads turned and he was greeted by shouts of 'Wotcha, mate,'
and 'All right Nobby?' He nodded or raised a thumb in answer
to the friendly greetings. This was his local and he recognised
a lot of faces from the factory.

There was a warm fire burning in the huge grate at one end of the large room and Harry's spirits lifted at the sight. He walked over to the bar and ordered a drink then turned and looked around for a place to sit.

'Wotcha Nobby.'

He recognised the voice; it was his friend Wally. 'You look soaked, Nobby, come over here by the fire.' Harry picked up his beer and was more than pleased to join his friend by the warm fire; he dropped his wet cap into the hearth to dry out, ran his fingers through his wet hair and set his drink on a nearby table.

'You all right, Mate?'

Wally had been a really good friend to Harry, especially since Lila had gone. Maisie, Wally's wife had sat in with the children many times so that the two men could go out for a pint. Now Harry saw the anxious look on Wally's kind face and shrugged. 'I'm all right Wal.'

'What are you looking so down about then? It's not like you.' Harry liked Wally; they had become more like brothers over the years.

'Oh, the same old thing, mate. I still haven't had anyone round about my advert. It's really getting me down. Every day seems to bring more problems.'

'But you put that card out ages ago; I would have thought there were hundreds of women looking for that kind of work. What's up with 'em?' Wally and his wife had no children of their own and were very fond of Harry's family.

'You can't blame them, Wal. Not many women want to take on five children and their old man.'

Wally smiled. 'Your lot aren't any trouble, Nobby. My missus says she'd have 'em like a shot if she was a bit younger, but what with her back she just couldn't manage the extra work.'

'Wally, Maisie does enough for us already. She's always sending pies and cakes and stuff round. I'll never be able to repay you both for all your kindness.'

'It's a pity that we can't do more, though.' Wally scratched his head. 'I wish there was something we could do.'

The two men sat still and silent for a while, both looking thoughtfully into the fire and sipping at their beers. The buzz of voices seemed far away, and the smell of wet clothes forgotten as they thought of other things. Eventually Harry laid his empty glass down and picked up his cap, which was now quite dry. 'Well, Wal, I must be going or the family will wonder where I am.' He put his cap on and stood up.

'Ta-ta, Wally, see you Monday.'

'Ta-ta, mate, don't worry too much.'

'I don't want you worrying about my problems either, Wal. I'm sure someone will turn up for me soon.'

The two friends shook hands. Harry crossed to the door and left the warm room and the comfort of the pub behind him, hoping that the rain had eased off. No such luck. It was still raining cats and dogs outside. Pulling up his collar, Harry sank his hands into his pockets and continued on his way.

Telling Wally he was sure someone would turn up was all very well. He was beginning to think that no woman in her right mind would want to be his housekeeper. He was only offering board and lodging after all. In return, he expected someone to do all the housework and look after the family. If only he could afford to pay a wage as well it might be different, but that was out of the question.

Harry had been so full of hope when he had first advertised for a housekeeper, now weeks later here they were and nothing had changed. No one had answered his advert and little Rosie was still pining for a mother.

Chapter 14

The sun began to shine just as Harry reached his front door. On the mantelshelf he found a note saying that Mary had taken Rosie to the park. The boys were nowhere to be seen; he guessed that they too had gone to the park and wondered whether they had found shelter from the rain.

When he had changed out of his wet clothes and made himself a pot of tea, he sat in his old wooden armchair; it was still the most comfortable chair in the house. Lila had made cushions for it; she'd said he deserved the extra comfort after working so hard all day. Now, sipping his hot tea Harry began to relax.

His attention was drawn to the painting. Lila couldn't have been more than four years old when it was painted but he could still see signs of the woman he had married. The eyes were kind and the mouth was relaxed, looking just as if she might be about to speak. He thought again of the day when she had told him she was expecting their child. She had been so very happy and the future had looked so bright. Yes, he did have a lovely little daughter, but her Mummy was not here to see her grow up. Life can be cruel.

Harry woke with a start. It must have been the noise of the key being dragged through the letterbox. Mary came into the room and plonked herself into the chair opposite Harry. He could tell that she wasn't very happy.

'Hello, duck, did you take Rosie to the park?'

'Yes and we had to go into one of the wooden shelters to get out of the rain.'

'I'm glad you found somewhere to shelter, it didn't half come down. I got soaked through coming home from the cemetery.' He heard the sound of feet on the stairs and guessed it was Rosie.

'Have you taken your shoes off, Rosie?' Mary spoke sharply to the little girl as she came into the room. 'Next time you want to go to the park you can get someone else to take you because I won't.'

Rosie stood there covered from head to foot in wet sand. She had obviousely been crying. 'If I had a Mummy she would have cleaned me up.'

'If you had come out of the sand pit when I told you, you wouldn't have got in such a mess. I'm fed up with looking after you. You never do anything I tell you.'

Harry got up from his chair and took Rosie by the hand. 'Come on, ducky, let's fill the bath up and wash some of that sand off.' He helped her out of the wet sandy clothing and put one of his warm work shirts around her. He brought the tin bath in from the garden, put it in front of the fire and filled it with the warm water that had been heating on the stove.

Later, when Rosie was bathed and fed and tucked up in her bed, Harry came down to have a word with Mary. She looked very unhappy, he was sure it must be more than the upset with Rosie.

By the time the boys arrived home, Harry and Mary had finished their little heart to heart. She'd burst into tears when he had asked her what was troubling her. She said, 'You wouldn't understand.' But eventually it all came out. Mary just needed some time on her own. Harry realised that all her free time was taken up with looking after Rosie and the rest of the family. Poor Mary, she had looked after them all practically since the day her mother had died. She worked so hard and hardly ever complained. Why hadn't he seen it before? He knew that little Rosie needed a mother but now he could see that Mary needed help even more.

Oh, how Harry wanted someone to come and be their housekeeper. All he could do was to hope, pray and wait.

Chapter 15

It was Friday and the five-forty-five train was carrying its load of work-weary passengers homeward. Sitting in a corner seat of the third carriage with her head bent was a slim, dark-haired girl; she was concentrating hard on the complicated pattern of a blouse she was making. She wanted this garment to be perfect.

There were six girls in Dolly's family and she was the youngest. When they were all very young they were taught to crochet as their mother thought 'it was a fitting pastime for a young lady'. This was by far the prettiest blouse that Dolly had made, the colour was a deep cream and it had a nice shell pattern all over it. When it was finished it would be just right for her to wear when she and George gave their good news to the family. Glancing out of the window, Dolly could see that the train was approaching her station. She briefly held her work up to admire it before folding it carefully away between sheets of tissue paper. She was very pleased with the blouse and just knew that George would like it too.

George was in the Army. He had been lodging with the family for some time; she had fallen for him at first sight, he was tall, dark and handsome and had the nicest smile that she had ever seen. Every time Dolly saw George in his uniform her heart missed a beat, he looked so smart and handsome; she was certain that every girl in the town envied her and wished that they were in her shoes. One week ago George had asked her to marry him and she had said yes straight away. He took her to a hotel where they ate a wonderful meal and he bought her red wine – it was the first time she had tasted wine. George leaned across the table and held her hand in his; he told her he loved her and gave her a small red box. She opened it to find a lovely silver comb. It was so romantic, she was absolutely certain that George was the man with whom she wanted to spend the rest of her life.

She was surprised to find that George had rented a room. There were rich velvet curtains at the windows and the bed was made up with cream satin sheets. They spent the whole evening together. They made love on the big bed. George said it was all right because they would soon be married. She hadn't mentioned anything about this to her parents. They wouldn't have understood.

Dolly's five sisters were all married, and now it was to be her turn. George was away for a week, he was due back on Sunday and when all the family were together they were going to announce their engagement. She could hardly wait for the day to come. Once the family had been told of the engagement, they could start planning for the wedding.

The wheels of the train screamed against the brakes and the long train gradually came to a stop. Dolly picked up her bag, opened the carriage door and stepped out on to the platform. She was glad to leave the smell and noise of the train behind her. She handed her ticket to the man at the gate. As she walked away she could hear the train huffing and puffing, getting steam up ready to continue on its journey.

Chapter 16

At long last Sunday arrived; Dolly was dressed in a new brown skirt, it went very well with the cream blouse that had just been finished in time. Her dark brown hair was piled up on top of her head and she was wearing the beautiful hair comb that George had given her. Taking one last critical look at her reflection in the mirror, she pinched her cheeks to make them glow, fluffed up the collar of her blouse and went down to where the rest of the family were waiting.

Everyone said how nice she looked; Dolly didn't really need to be told because she had seen it in the mirror. She was twenty-six, slim and quite pretty, and, best of all, she was about to embark on a new life with George.

George was due to arrive at about five o'clock. The table was laid with all the special food that her mother and the girls had prepared and everything and everyone was ready and waiting.

Dolly's sisters were telling their mother and each other about their children, the men had hung the dartboard on the kitchen door and were playing a noisy game. It was a nice change for Father to have the men around. He had long ago realised that he was outnumbered by all the women in his life. Sometimes the girls came when their husbands were at work. At these times their father would make himself scarce by going into the garden. He just couldn't get excited about the latest fashions or the baby getting a new tooth.

The living room clock struck six and there was still no sign of George. Mother said that they should begin the meal without him. They were all of the same opinion that he had missed his train. The meal was eaten and the table cleared. Dolly had not managed to swallow a thing; she was very worried about George's absence but her mother said, 'Perhaps he thought you meant next week, dear,' but Dolly was sure that George had known exactly which day. He had said 'See you Sunday, Doll,' and when she asked if she should meet him at the station he had said no because he would have a surprise and wanted to give it to her at home. Dolly was sure that the surprise he spoke of was going to be her engagement ring.

Later, when the sisters and their families had left and her parents had gone to bed, Dolly sat alone for a long time, the handkerchief in her hand soaked in tears. She heard the sound of her mother's light footstep on the stairs and quickly dried her eyes.

Dolly's mother Jessie was a sweet, kindly little woman, with the same pale blue eyes as Dolly and a gentle voice. She laid an arm around her youngest daughter's shoulders. 'Why don't you go to bed dear? It's very late, I'm sure that if George were coming, he would have been here long ago; perhaps his leave was cancelled for some reason. I expect he'll write to you.'

Dolly looked up at her mother. 'Perhaps you're right, Mum, but I'm so disappointed. Today was going to be so special. I think George was going to give me my engagement ring whilst all the family were here.' She blew her nose and dried her eyes again.

'Never mind, dear. Now go to bed or you'll be too tired for work in the morning. If George does give you a ring the girls will see it when they come next time.'

Reluctantly, Dolly stood up, kissed her mother on the cheek

and slowly made her way up to bed. Perhaps Jessie was right and George's leave had been cancelled. She would receive a letter from him in a day or two.

Sleep did not come easily to Dolly; she tossed and turned and managed to drop into a light sleep only in the early hours of the next morning.

When the postman came early next morning, there was no letter from George. Dolly went off to work with a heavy heart. The next day was the same, she couldn't write to him as she had no idea where he was. When he'd left a week earlier he just said that he had to go away for a few days. He hadn't said where he was going.

Dolly worked in a hospital for disabled servicemen. She enjoyed the work, it was very rewarding to be able to help and comfort the men who had fought for their country so bravely. At the hospital Dolly was on the go most of the time but after lunch she would go to the restroom and chat to some of the patients. Some of the men were far from home and were desperate to get back. One man named Stan had been in the same regiment as George. She often sat with him after lunch as he seemed very friendly. He wasn't there when Dolly went into the room, and had not arrived by the time she went back to her duties.

At the end of her shift Dolly left for home on her usual train. Today there was no blouse to work on and she spent the time staring out of the window, wondering where George was, what he was doing and if he had written to her. On reaching the house she was disappointed to find that there was still no letter.

That night Dolly went to bed early. She told her parents that she had a headache. She knew she wasn't going to be very good company and felt the need to be alone.

In the early days before all the sisters had married it would not have been possible for Dolly to have time alone. There were so many of them and they had to share bedrooms. Now, though, she could shut her bedroom door and have some privacy. She tried to read but found that it was impossible to concentrate. Where was George, and why hadn't she heard from him?

Chapter 17

Dolly was at the hospital preparing to start her shift, standing in the small room where the nurses kept their personal belongings. There had been no letter for her in the morning post and she was feeling down in the dumps. Suddenly, the door burst open and her friend Ann came in like a whirlwind – everything Ann did was in double-quick time, she even talked faster than anyone else. Ann had been working the night shift.

'Hello, Doll!' She was in her usual rush and her words came out fast and furious. 'What a night! Some of the chaps who are leaving today were talking till about three this morning. You'd think they'd said all there was to say to each other after spending so much time together recuperating. But they were talking and exchanging addresses till the wee small hours.'

Ann chatted on and on whilst changing into her outdoor clothes; she hardly seemed to stop for breath. 'Well, I'm off home. Bye Dolly,' then she swept out of the room. No sooner had Ann gone, than she was back again. 'Doll, I nearly forgot to tell you. Stan was asking for you. He's leaving this afternoon and wants to see you before he goes. He'll be in the rest room at lunch time.' Then she was gone again.

When Dolly had finished the morning shift she tidied her hair and made her way to the rest room. Stan was sitting with another man over by the window. As soon as he saw her he excused himself and came over. Dolly thought Stan had just wanted to say goodbye and she was surprised to see him looking so serious. She thought he would have been pleased to be leaving for home.

'Hello nurse, I have a message from George.' Dolly's heart skipped a beat and she was trembling. Stan took her arm and led her over to a quiet corner where they both sat down. 'What is it Stan, is George all right? Was his leave cancelled? Has he had to stay on for a few days?' She realised that she was gabbling, but just couldn't stop herself.

'No, it's nothing like that. I'm sorry, nurse, but George isn't coming back at all. He's going to write to you, he asked me to tell you that he's sorry, but he won't be seeing you again.'

Dolly's heart was pounding now. 'Does he want me to go to him? We're getting engaged, you know.'

'Well, he will write to you and explain everything. It's not really for me to say, but he says he can't marry you. I am so sorry to be the one to give you this kind of news but I promised George I would. I really have to leave now, nurse, or I'll miss my train. Goodbye, I hope everything turns out all right for you.' He touched her arm gently, and left the room.

Suddenly, the room seemed very cold. Dolly was unable to stop shaking. The ward Sister found her there some time later still staring into space. One of the other nurses kindly volunteered to take her home.

Chapter 18

It was two months on. Her father had finished shouting. Her mother had come to terms with the news. The tears were all shed and Dolly began to think about what she was going to do with her life. It had been a shock to everyone, especially Dolly, but when the letter from George did arrive it was even more shocking to read that he had gone back to a wife and family in Scotland. Dolly wanted to forget that George had ever come into her life, but then she discovered she was pregnant with his child, and that had changed everything.

There was a very unpleasant court case; Walter had insisted that George be charged with breach of promise. George denied ever promising Dolly anything; he said it could not be his child as they had never slept together. Dolly was not wearing his ring, so the case was dropped. The whole thing had been very embarrassing, Dolly was just glad that it was all over.

In September, a beautiful baby girl was born and she was christened Ivy. As time passed she grew into a lovely dark-haired little charmer. Dolly went back to work as soon as she was able, leaving her mother to care for the baby.

Every day she looked forward to coming home from work when she would see her child and hold her in her arms. Now that she was back at work she saw little enough of her baby and so looked forward to those few precious moments before she tucked her darling up for the night. She loved little Ivy to bits and valued every minute that they were able to spend together.

One day Dolly came home from work and found much to her disappointment that her mother had already put little Ivy to bed. She found Jessie in the small scullery preparing the evening meal; she kissed her lightly on the cheek and asked why her baby had already been put to bed. 'Is she ill, Mum, has she got a temperature?'

Jessie turned to her daughter and saw the worried look on her face. 'There's nothing to worry about, dear, I just think that if Ivy waits until you come home from work, it is rather late for her bedtime.'

Dolly was relieved to hear that there was nothing wrong with her baby and said so but she wasn't very happy about her mother putting Ivy to bed. 'Mum, the only time I see her on my work days is in the evening before she is put to bed. Please don't put her down before I come home.'

Jessie turned back to preparing the meal. 'She needs her sleep, dear. It's a good thing to start as you mean to go on.'

'Mum, she can sleep at any time, she's a baby.'

'Baby or not,' said her mother, 'she gets over-tired.'

Although Dolly was angry and disappointed she did not want an argument. It was kind of her mother to care for her baby whilst she was at work but she made a mental note to discuss the matter at a later date.

'Well, I'll just go up and give her a kiss.' Dolly made to leave the room but her mother put a hand on her arm.

'Now, dear, that's not a good idea, is it? You'll only disturb her and then she won't want to go back to sleep again.'

'Mum, I want to tuck her in,' and that said Dolly gently pushed passed her mother and made her way upstairs to her bedroom.

Little Ivy was not in her bedroom and Dolly was amazed to find that her cot had been moved into a small box room which had until then been used as a store room. There were tears in her eyes as she gently touched the baby's soft face with her lips. She loved to hear the sound of little Ivy's breathing as she lay in the cot beside her bed at night, but now her mother had moved her into the box room, she would not be able to hear or see her baby in the night and she was sure that she would lay awake just wondering how her child was, sleeping alone in that little room.

Another day when Dolly came home with a pretty bonnet for Ivy, her mother refused to let her wear it, saying that 'the colour wasn't right for her'. It seemed to Dolly that her mother was treating Ivy as if she were her own child; in fact many visitors to the house thought that Jessie was indeed Ivy's mother.

When Ivy was just eighteen months old she started to talk. Dolly had just come in from work and as she was about to enter the room she heard her mother say, 'Dolly will be home soon, darling.' Dolly was very upset, she reminded Jessie that Ivy was *her* child and she wanted her to know it. Jessie smiled, 'Oh, dear, don't worry about little things like that. It doesn't matter if she calls you Dolly; it is your name, after all. She hears me using it, so it's only natural that she should as well.'

Jessie meant well, Dolly knew that, but she wanted to care for her little girl herself and that was what she intended to do. Ivy was her child; she wanted her to know that *she* was her mother and not just a sister or some sort of aunt. From that moment on Dolly made her mind up to find a new place to live where she and Ivy could be together without the constant interference from her mother.

Chapter 19

It was Dolly's day off from work. She had bathed her little girl and was about to put a dress on her when Jessie came into the room, took the dress from Dolly's hand and brought another one from the drawer. 'I want her to wear the blue one today, Dolly; she had a pink one on yesterday.' Dolly was annoyed at her mother's interference but decided to let it go, she didn't want to argue today. She finished dressing Ivy and took her downstairs to put her into the pram. She was going to visit her friend Mary. Mary had not seen Dolly for a while and had invited her over for a chat.

Just as Dolly was putting the pram covers on Jessie came out into the hallway. 'Where are you going, Dolly? I want Ivy to stay here this morning, her Aunty May is coming to visit.'

'Oh, I'm sorry, Mum but I promised to go over to Mary's. We haven't met up in ages.'

'But I have asked May over especially to see our baby so you will have to go without her, dear.'

Dolly could hardly believe her ears. 'Mum, Ivy is not *our* baby, she is *my* baby, and May will have to see her some other time because we are going to Mary's.'

Dolly saw the hurt look on her mother's face but somehow she had to stop her from treating Ivy as her own child.

'Bye Mum, I'm not sure what time I'll be home. If Mary asks us to stay to tea, we'll stay.' With that, Dolly left the house.

Dolly enjoyed the day with her friend. She loved the fact that she was with her baby without the constant interference of her mother. She told Mary all about the situation at home with her mother, and said that she was worried that her baby would grow up thinking that Jessie was her mother, not her grandmother. Mary saw the tears in Dolly's eyes and she put an arm around her friend's shoulders. She didn't like to see how upset she was. 'Dolly, why don't you look for a place of your own? It would solve everything.'

Dolly said she had been thinking along the same lines.

'But it isn't possible, Mary; I would still need to earn enough money to keep Ivy and myself. I couldn't even go out to work if I had to care for a baby, then of course there would be rent to pay as well. No, I'm afraid it's out of the question.'

Suddenly Mary had an idea. 'Dolly,' she said, 'How would you feel about living in with another family if it meant that you didn't have to go out to work?'

Dolly smiled. 'I suppose you're thinking that one of my sisters would take me in, but they wouldn't dare go against the wishes of my parents, and I would still have to find the money for our keep, wouldn't I?'

'No, I was thinking of something my aunt said the other day, Dolly, about a friend of hers who is in need of a house-keeper. It occurred to me that something like that might solve your problem. It would provide you with a home, and you wouldn't have to go out to work, would you?'

'Well, yes, that would be an idea, but I still have little Ivy to care for, don't I? They might not like to have a young baby about the house, and they would probably want me to be at their beck and call all the time. That wouldn't be possible: after all, the reason for my leaving home is because I want to spend time with Ivy.'

Dolly burst into tears. Her situation was impossible. It seemed as if she would have to stay with her parents and keep working at the hospital after all.

Mary was getting quite excited now. 'Listen, Dolly, the friend my Aunt was talking about has got children of his own. You could look after them and Ivy at the same time.'

The two young women talked on until quite late into the evening. Dolly eventually dried her eyes and thought that perhaps there might be a light at the end of the tunnel. When she at last said goodbye to Mary she was feeling much more positive. She was determined to write for an interview for the housekeeper's job.

Yes, things seemed to be looking up for Dolly and her little girl after all.

Chapter 20

Harry had almost resigned himself to the fact that no one wanted to be his housekeeper. The children were growing up and three of them were now working. They still needed caring for and of course meals had to be prepared. Mary had taken a job in the canteen at the sugar factory, she was in her element. She had been cooking meals for the family for several years now and was a very good cook. One thing Mary disliked about her job in the canteen was being told what to do all the time; she was not used to following orders.

'I can't stand her, Uncle Harry, she's so bossy.' Mary was sitting with her elbows on the table and her chin in her hands. 'Every time I turn around she's looking at me, I'm fed up with it.' She was telling Harry about her day and by all accounts it had been very stressful. There was a new canteen manager. She had been picking on Mary from the time she started in the morning till the whistle had gone for the end of the shift in the evening.

Harry tried to comfort her. 'You'll get used to her, duck, don't worry so much. When she realises what a good worker you are she'll soon get off your back.'

'Well, if she keeps it up I'm leaving, so there!' Mary got up and left the room in a huff. Harry sighed. The boys he could cope with but he really didn't understand girls. When Mary was younger she was easy to look after and he always got on well with her, but since she had turned sixteen she had been so moody. She was not the same from one day to the next.

Harry had been taught that if he had respect for his elders and worked hard then everything would be all right. Mary wasn't about to respect the new canteen manager and Harry had a feeling that she would rather give up her job than take any more orders, but he knew she was a good little worker so they would just have to wait and see.

Young Charlie was still enjoying his work on the barges and Albert was getting on fine in a local factory. Billy was a bit of a handful, he hated going to school and bunked off at every opportunity. He was nearly twelve now and Harry never knew if he was at school or not. He left the house in the morning at the same time as Rosie and came home at the same time too, but the School Board man came around a couple of times, saying that the teacher hadn't seen Billy for days.

Rosie! Well, she lived in a world of her own, always imagining that she had a mother like the other children. She would tell Harry that her mother was going to do this or that for her when she came home. In the beginning, Harry tried to say that it wasn't true, but it usually ended in tears so now he just let her get on with it. She seemed happy enough.

One Sunday near the end of June, Harry and Rosie were outside in the back yard enjoying the sunshine. He was mending a fence; Rosie was putting her doll to bed in an old wooden box. The boys and Mary had gone out. Harry put down the hammer he had been using, and sat down on the back step. He leaned against the doorframe and closed his eyes. With the warm sun on his face he could almost imagine that he was in the country somewhere. They hadn't been to the country for years; he wouldn't know how to go about it on his own. Well of course the older children would be able to help him carry things but he wouldn't know what to take. Lila had always sorted that kind of thing out. Harry still couldn't read very well, he never had to write to anyone and wasn't sure that he could even put a letter together.

Suddenly, Harry was shaken from his daydreaming by Rosie. 'Daddy! Daddy! There's a lady at the door.' He jumped to his feet and went through to the front of the house.

Harry didn't recognise the young woman; he thought she had probably come to the wrong house. 'Can I help you, duck, who are you looking for?' She was quite pretty and must have been about ten years younger than him; she had the palest of blue eyes and looked very nervous. Harry asked the question again. 'Who are you looking for, duck?'

At last she found her voice. 'Are you Mr Kain? I was told that I'd find Mr Kain at this address.'

'Yes, that's me, love, what can I do for you?'

'I was told by a friend of mine that you were looking for a housekeeper, was she right?' Harry couldn't believe his ears. 'Yes, yes, that's right I am, but there are rather a lot of us, it would be a lot of work for a young woman like you.' Harry couldn't believe that this young person would want to work as a housekeeper for his big family. 'Er, well, what I mean is, it would probably suit someone a bit older.'

Once Dolly had gathered her courage, she followed Harry into the house where she was introduced to a small girl whose name was Rosie. (Rosie spent the whole of the time Dolly was in the house hiding behind her father's chair.)

Over a cup of tea she told Mr Kain her plight. He became quite concerned when she told him that she had a child of her own. 'But that would mean there would be eight altogether for you to look after. Do you think you could manage that?' She didn't look very strong to Harry, and although he liked the sound of this young woman, he wouldn't want her to take his large family on if it was going to be too much for her.

An hour later Dolly got up to leave. She shook Harry's outstretched hand and agreed to come over one evening in the week to meet the rest of the family. When the door had closed behind her she felt like skipping along the street. Mr Kain was such a pleasant man, he was a bit of a rough diamond but Dolly liked him and she was sure they would be able to get along. She could hardly wait until Wednesday when she was to meet the whole family. Meanwhile Harry could not believe his luck. To think that at last someone had answered his call for help!

'No, I'm not staying home,' Mary was standing her ground. 'I'm going to Annie's after work. She's got a new gramophone and some records she is going to play for me.'

'Oh, come on, duck, I want you to meet this lady, it's important. You know I won't ask her to stay if you couldn't get on with her, that wouldn't be fair on either of you.' Harry smiled at her. 'You know, Mary, if she does come to look after us you will be able to go out with Annie more often, and it would save you having to look after the young 'uns when I'm not here.'

Mary liked the sound of that.

'Oh, all right. I'll just have to explain to Annie tomorrow, but if this woman is too bossy I don't want her here.' Mary plonked herself down on to a chair, her lips were pressed tightly together and her whole attitude said, 'I'm not going to like her.'

Harry breathed a sigh of relief; the boys had already agreed to stay home, now the whole family would be there to meet this young lady who could possibly save his sanity by becoming their housekeeper. The fact was, he had already made up his mind that this young person was right for the job.

Chapter 21

Dolly said nothing to her parents about applying for the position of housekeeper. They would only have tried to talk her out of it, but her mind was made up. When she informed her mother that she would be taking little Ivy out on Wednesday evening there was an argument just as she had expected.

'Her bedtime is six o'clock, Dolly. If she's out after that time it will upset her routine.' Dolly's mother went on to say that it was irresponsible of her to take the baby out in the evening air. 'It'll be me that has to comfort her when she is upset or gets the sniffles.'

Dolly would have liked to have said 'not for much longer' but she resisted the temptation. 'Don't worry, mother. I'll wrap her up so that she doesn't get a chill.' Her mother wanted to know where she was going. She just said that she was going to visit a friend and left it at that. After all, she hadn't been given the job yet.

It was still early evening when Dolly arrived at the small house where she was hoping to live and work. She took Ivy out of the pram, reached up and pressed the bell, then stepped back and waited for the door to be opened. When it did open she was surprised to see a slim young man of about fifteen smiling down at her.

'Hello, I'm Albert. Please come in.' Albert stepped aside and allowed Dolly to pass into the narrow hallway. 'Is this your baby? She's nice, isn't she? What's her name?' The questions came one after the other so fast that there was no time for Dolly to answer any of them before they reached the living room.

Looking around the room Dolly saw all eyes upon her. Besides the young man who had opened the door, there was a young woman, another older boy and a younger boy of about eleven. You could have cut the silence with a knife.

'Hello, I'm Dolly Talbot and this is Ivy.'

The young woman spoke first. 'Uncle Harry's in the garden. Rosie's gone to fetch him.' She had hardly finished speaking when Harry burst into the room, spilling out apologies as he came.

'I'm so sorry, duck; I should have been here to introduce you to the family. I was just trying to collect the cabbages before the caterpillars get to them. Put the kettle on, Mary, there's a good girl and make the young lady a cup of tea.' Harry gently ushered young Billy out of the big chair and after plumping up the cushion indicated for Dolly to sit in it.

'This is Billy. Come and say hello, Billy.' But Billy stayed exactly where he was, his hands held tightly behind his back.

''Ello.'

'Hello, Billy, I'm very pleased to meet you.'

'And this is Albert.'

'Hello. We've met, haven't we, Albert?' Dolly noticed that big smile again as Albert answered. 'Yes. I let you in, didn't I, Miss?' The other older boy stepped forward and awkwardly shook Dolly's hand. 'I'm Charlie, Miss; I'm the eldest, pleased to meet you.'

Harry called out to Mary, 'Come in and say hello, Mary.' Mary's voice came back from the other room. 'I'm busy, I'll be there in a minute,' then Dolly heard her say 'Go on, go in,

will you?' Almost at once the pretty little girl that she had seen
on her previous visit came into the room. She must have been
six or seven with big blue eyes and brown curly hair tumbling
around her shoulders. She stood just inside the door looking
at Dolly; Dolly could see that she was very shy.

'Hello, you're Rosie, aren't you?' Rosie was nervously twisting
her fingers together and rocking on to the outside edges of
her shoes, and made no reply.

'This is my little girl, her name is Ivy. Won't you come and
say hello to her?' Hearing her name, Ivy decided she had been
quiet for too long and said, 'Ivy, 'llo.' At this Rosie came over
and gave the baby a kiss. She looked hard and long at Dolly
and eventually said, 'Are you going to be my mummy?'

Well, the ice was broken and suddenly everyone seemed to
be speaking at once. Dolly was told all about the boys' work
and Billy showed her his picture book. Rosie was really taken
with Ivy, she brought a ball out and they began rolling it across
the floor to each other.

Mary came in with the tea and some cake she had made,
and then introduced herself. She was friendly enough, but
somehow she was different from the others. Although she joined
in the conversation, she didn't offer any more information than
was absolutely necessary. Dolly put this down to the fact that
there had not been another woman in the house for a long
time. Perhaps Mary wasn't sure that she wanted one now.

The evening went off quite well and by the time Dolly had
to leave, she felt sure that she could be happy with this family.
Arrangements were made for Dolly to come over when the
family were out. She and Harry needed to talk in private about
the possibility of her being his housekeeper.

Harry and Dolly got on very well at their next meeting.
They were both relieved to find that they had a lot in common.

Harry took her over the small house and she saw the bedroom she would be sharing with her daughter. It was the largest bedroom in the house and had up until then been Harry's. Harry was to move into the boys' room and would sleep with Billy.

When Dolly had seen over the house and small garden, Harry made a pot of tea and they both sat silently for a while. Dolly liked the little house and felt that she and Ivy could be comfortable there. The place had been kept fairly neat and tidy and Dolly felt sure that with Mary's help she would be able to cope with the large family. She wasn't afraid of hard work. There had only been three adults and the baby at home in her father's house but she had always done most of the housework when she was home at the weekends.

Harry sat patiently watching as Dolly sipped her tea. After a while he felt that if he didn't speak he would burst. 'Well, duck, what do you think?'

Dolly looked at him and smiled. 'Mr Kain, I can hardly believe that you really want me and Ivy to come to live with you and your young family. As I said to you earlier I've never been a housekeeper. I do hope that I won't be a disappointment to you all.'

Harry could see tears in her eyes. 'Please call me Harry, and I'd like to call you Dolly, if that's all right.'

'Yes, yes, of course, *Harry*. I expect it will take time for me to get used to everything.'

'We won't be disappointed in you, Dolly. We have waited such a long time for someone to help us out. It's hard to believe we're lucky enough to get someone like you. In fact, Mary was sure that when we did get a housekeeper, she'd turn out to be an awful dragon. We've been struggling for a long time, I did have doubts about bringing a stranger into the house, but now that you have come along, Dolly, I'm sure that everything will turn out fine.'

Arrangements were made for Dolly to start her new life as soon as possible. She left Harry with joy in her heart and a spring in her step, looking forward to the challenge of the future.

Chapter 22

The hospital agreed to Dolly leaving with just one week's notice. She wanted to start in her new employment with the Kain family as soon as possible. She had worked at the hospital for a long time and been very happy in her work. She had also made many friends; she would now have to leave them behind. She was a good nurse, working at the hospital had been very fulfilling for her and she would be sad to leave. She had, in some small way, brightened the lives of the many brave servicemen who came into the hospital for healing or convalescence.

The important thing to Dolly now was that she was going to be a real mother to her daughter, bringing her up as she thought best, without interference from her parents. When Ivy was first born, it had seemed the ideal solution for her mother to care for her baby. Dolly had been able to go to the hospital every day with the knowledge that Ivy was in safe hands. However, she had come to realise that it wasn't at all what she wanted, neither was it what her baby needed. Ivy needed her mother whilst she was growing up, and Dolly wanted to be with her child. Now it was going to happen, thanks to Mr Kain and his family.

So far Dolly had said nothing to her parents about her move. She knew they were going to be upset so she left it as long as possible before telling them, but now it would have to be done.

On Wednesday when Dolly arrived home from her shift at the hospital, the table was being laid for the evening meal. Her mother had kept the baby up late for a change to allow Dolly to see her before she was put to bed.

Dolly played for a while with her child, and then she took her up to the bedroom and sang quietly to her until she went off to sleep. Looking down at her sleeping child she had to fight back the tears. This was what she had been missing, but she would be tucking little Ivy up every single night when she started her new life in a few days' time. She could hardly wait. She decided to break the news to her parents that very evening.

The meal was over at last. Dolly had not eaten a thing; she had spent the whole meal just pushing the food around her plate. There had been a lump in her throat throughout the meal; it had prevented her from swallowing even a morsel. The fear at what her parents would say when they heard the news was upsetting her more than she would ever have imagined.

Dolly was helping to wash the dishes when her mother turned to her and said. 'Are you feeling unwell, dear? You didn't eat much tonight.'

'No, mum, I wasn't very hungry, and I have something to tell you.'

'Oh dear, that sounds serious, Dolly, I'm sure it can't be that bad.'

They finished putting the dishes away and went out into the garden. It was such a nice evening and her mother thought it a pity to spend it indoors. Dolly's father was already relaxing in his old garden chair smoking his pipe. Looking at him, it seemed to Dolly as though he didn't have a care in the world. She wondered if he would look so contented when he had heard her news.

The two women sat together on the rickety garden bench. Dolly could still remember her father making the bench many years ago when she was quite a small girl. She'd had a happy childhood and felt sad that she was now about to leave her parents and the family home with all the things that were so dear to her.

She was going to live in a strange house to care for someone else's family, moving away from all those familiar things she had grown up with. Dolly had to quickly remind herself of the reason for her move, she must have no regrets. In her new home she would be with her daughter all day and every day. Remembering how kind Mr Kain had been she felt better at once.

The garden was full of flowers. Her father was a very keen gardener and for most of the summer the garden would be full of colour. The house where Mr Kain lived did have a garden but it was very small, not a patch on this one of her father's. Dolly knew that there were a lot of things she was going to miss.

Looking at her mother sitting there with her eyes closed against the sun, now low in the sky, and her father chewing on the stem of his old pipe, Dolly felt sorry that she was going to cause an upset by telling them her news, but it was now or never.

'Mum and Dad,' she said, 'I'm going to start a new job next week and it will mean that I'll be moving away.'

Her mother opened her eyes and turned to look at Dolly as if she was not sure that she had heard correctly.

'Move away? What do you mean, dear?'

Her father took the pipe from his mouth.

'Move away? Don't be silly, Dolly, where would you go?'

'Well, I'm going as housekeeper to a family in the East End.'

'You can't do that, dear. You would miss little Ivy too much if you moved away, and she would miss you too.'

'I'll be taking Ivy with me, Mum. I'm doing it so that I can spend more time with her. We will be together all the time, instead of just for a few minutes in the evening and at weekends.'

Dolly saw the sudden fear in her mother's eyes. She realised at that moment that her mother really had looked on Ivy as her own child, and had thought she would live with them forever. Her mother's eyes filled with tears. 'But you can't do that, Dolly, you can't.'

'I'm sorry, Mum, but it's all arranged, I will be going next week.' Her mother stood up and rushed into the house. Dolly made to follow but her father caught her arm.

'You know this will break your mother's heart, don't you? How can you be so hard-hearted as to take the child away from her now?'

Dolly turned to face her father and saw that he too had tears in his eyes.

'I'm sorry, Dad, I don't want to hurt you both but Ivy is my baby. I want to be with her as she is growing up. The only way to make that possible is for me to get work where I can have her with me all the time and still have enough money for us to live on. That's why I have to do this.'

Dolly turned away from her father and went into the house; he did not follow her but stayed outside in the garden, sadly puffing away at his pipe.

That evening was one of the longest that she could remember but there didn't seem to be anything else to say or do. Her mother had shut herself in her bedroom and her father sat in the garden until it was quite dark. Dolly went to bed with a very heavy heart.

Next day she tried to speak to her mother but Jessie just

busied about preparing the breakfast, clattering dishes, never meeting her eyes once. Her lips were pressed tightly together. Dolly could tell just by looking at her that it would not be possible to hold any sort of sensible conversation.

It was hard for her to go off to work without trying again to talk to her mother. Dolly so wanted her mother to understand her need to be with little Ivy, she wanted to tell her that there was no other reason, but it was not to be. She left for work still feeling very upset about how badly her parents had taken the news.

Chapter 23

As the day drew near for Dolly to leave the home she had lived in all her life, she wondered if the step she was about to take was the right one. Dolly loved her parents dearly and was extremely grateful for all they had done for her. When she had first discovered that she was pregnant, they stood by her and supported her in her decision to keep the baby. Some girls in that position would have been turned out of the house, or made to put the child up for adoption, but her parents although disappointed, had stuck by her out of love, she was very aware of that. She had to think of some way of thanking them for all they had done for her.

When at last the day of the move arrived and there was no change in the attitude of her parents, Dolly sat down and wrote them a letter. She just had to tell them all the things that she had wanted to say before she left.

'Dear Mum and Dad,' she wrote,

I love you both dearly and that will never change, but I must get on with my life now and take full responsibility for my daughter.

You have been so good to us. I don't deserve your love and I realise that I have been very fortunate in the way that you stood by me when I needed you most. Please forgive me for taking little Ivy away from you. I will never let her forget you and we will visit whenever we can. You will always be her Grandparents and she will still love you in the same way.

I wish that I could hug you both before I leave but at the moment I can see that you are hurting too much. Thank you for all that you have done for me during my twenty-eight years. I will always remember you both in my prayers.

Your ever loving daughter,

Dolly.

She sealed the envelope and left it on the dining room table.

Dolly was ready to go, she just had to dress her baby and put the last of her things into a bag, so she went back upstairs to get Ivy ready. When this was done, she carefully carried the little girl downstairs and strapped her into her pram.

Her parents were sitting in the lounge, the door was open and her letter was open on the table. Dolly called 'Goodbye' from the hallway; they did not answer or even turn around to look at her.

'We're going now, Mum, I'll just leave Ivy here for you to kiss her while I get my bags from upstairs.' She left the baby just inside the doorway and went to the stairs, her foot had hardly touched the first stair when she heard a sound and on turning saw her father.

'I'll fetch the bags, you go in and say goodbye to your mother,' his voice sounded rather hoarse and she realised that he was fighting back the tears. Dolly turned and before she knew it was enfolded in her mother's arms. Then they were both crying and saying sorry. Jessie dabbed at her eyes and wiped her spectacles on her pinafore. She took both of Dolly's hands in hers and said 'Dolly, there will always be a home here for you and little Ivy. If things don't work out you will come back, won't you?' Dolly nodded. There was so much that she wanted to say but the tears were too close and she was too emotional to speak. She gave her mother another hug; it was wonderful to know that they would be parting in this way and not, as she had feared it might be, with animosity between them.

When her father came down with the bags he kissed Dolly on the forehead and gave her an envelope. 'Open it later,' he said. He had always been a man of few words. Dolly understood and knew that he had forgiven her. She was happier now and could leave for her new life knowing that her parents understood her reason for leaving them; they also knew that she loved them dearly.

As Dolly got nearer to the place that was to be her new home she became aware of the area; it was quite the poorest place that she had ever seen. The first time she had come to visit she had been so nervous that she'd hardly noticed the rundown houses and the raggedy children playing in the streets, but now she realised that this place was very different from the home she had just left.

Dolly resolved there and then that it would make no difference at all to her and Ivy's happiness with the Kain family. She stepped out with a light step and a song in her heart determined to make a go of the new life that lay ahead.

Chapter 24

It took some time for the family to get used to Dolly, but after a few months it was as if she had always been there. Rosie was delighted to tell all her friends and indeed everyone she met that she now had a new mother. At first, the neighbours got the wrong end of the stick when they saw a strange young woman in the Kain household. Tongues began to wag, but they soon discovered that Dolly was Harry's new housekeeper. At last, he had someone to help him to care for his family.

Before long, Dolly was arranging outings for them all. The older children were off with their own friends most of the time but Rosie, Billy and of course little Ivy always went along. It felt like any other family with two parents, although the children knew that it wasn't quite the same. It was nice for Harry to have some adult female company. He enjoyed being with Dolly, she had a good sense of humour and was very easy to talk to.

The two older boys loved having Dolly around, she wasn't as bossy as Mary, *and* she 'picked up' after them. This was the one thing that Mary had refused to do.

Charlie, Mary and Albert were all in work now, collecting a wage at the end of the week. The boys spent most of their free time with their friends. Mary too spent more time out in the evenings, but it was one special person that she was with, and it wasn't a girlfriend either. Fred was the apple of her eye.

She had met him at a friend's birthday party several months before. They were secretly planning to get married. Mary hadn't mentioned this to her uncle yet and was not sure just how he would take it. She was soon to find out.

'Uncle Harry, this is Fred.'

Mary had spoken to Dolly about Fred, and between them, they had decided that he should be invited to tea. Now here he was. Harry shook hands with the young man and they made polite conversation until it was time for tea. Mary couldn't eat; she was too worried about what Harry would say when he heard her news. When the meal was finished the two women cleared the table and went into the scullery to wash the dishes.

The washing-up done and the dishes put tidily away in the cupboard, Mary and Dolly joined the men once again.

'What's this I hear about you getting wed, duck?' Harry's remark took Mary off guard, and expecting an argument she jumped in with both feet.

'You can't stop us, Uncle Harry, we are going to do it whatever you say.'

'Calm down, Mary, calm down. I haven't said anything about stopping you, have I?'

Dolly patted a chair and beckoned to Mary. 'Come and sit here, dear.'

She could see that the young woman was expecting trouble. Mary sat down on the very edge of the chair; it was as if she was ready to spring up at the slightest provocation.

Harry smiled at her. 'Now listen, duck, you know I'm fond of you, don't you? You're like my own daughter. I wouldn't want to see you do anything that you'll regret later. I just want to ask young Fred here a few questions.'

Fred got up from his seat and went over to stand by Mary.

'Mr Kain, Mary and I do love one another, and I will always look after her.'

Harry looked at the young man standing there with his hand on Mary's shoulder. His eyes were kind and his touch seemed to relax Mary. It was obvious that he thought a great deal of her, and you only had to look into Mary's eyes to see that she adored him.

'Where will you live, son? I'm afraid there won't be room here with us because Mary is already sharing a room with Rosie. Does your mother have room for you both in her house?'

'I wouldn't like to start our married life living in someone else's house, Mr Kain. We are going to find a place of our own. I've seen two empty houses down Woolwich way. If you say that it's all right for us to marry, me and Mary will go over and look at them tomorrow.'

Mary's mouth dropped open in surprise.

'Fred! You never said anything to me.'

'Well, I didn't say, in case things didn't work out with your uncle.'

Harry could see that they were serious about the marriage but he hadn't finished yet. 'What sort of work do you, do Fred? Have you got a trade?'

'Well, I'm working in the steel works, sir, and it looks as if I might be made up to foreman soon.' Fred seemed to grow two inches before he said, 'I've already been to see the guv'ner and he says I've got a good chance.'

Harry smiled. 'Will you be able to afford the rent on a house though? And what if a family comes along? Do you think you'll cope then?'

'Oh Harry! Can't you see that they love one another?' Dolly couldn't stand by any more. She could see the tears welling up in Mary's eyes. She knew that anything Harry said would make little or no difference to Mary's plans for the future.

Harry argued that Mary was too young, and said that she didn't know how to handle money. He had one or two other objections as well but Dolly calmed him down and in the end he gave his consent for the young couple to get engaged.

Three months later, in a small church around the corner, Mary and her young man were joined in holy matrimony. The neighbours came out to see them off. Rosie was bridesmaid and Ivy gave Mary a pretty silver horseshoe for luck.

When the celebration party was over, Mary and Fred moved into their small rented terraced house in Abbey Wood. The young couple had been married less than a year when their first baby, a little boy, arrived. He was named Charles.

Mary proved to be a very good mother. This wasn't surprising, considering all the experience she had gained through looking after her brothers and Rosie.

Chapter 25

Dolly had lived with the Kain family for about six months when Harry surprised her one evening by proposing marriage. 'Will you marry me, duck?' She was sitting quietly mending and was sure that he couldn't actually have said the words that she thought she heard. She looked up from her sewing and across at Harry. He was obviously waiting for an answer to his question.

'What did you say, Harry?' When Harry repeated the question the words were exactly the same. 'Will you marry me, duck?'

Dolly was taken aback. She was very fond of Harry; he was kind and considerate, though a bit rough around the edges.

They talked until the small hours and the more they talked the more Dolly was sure it would be the right thing to do. 'You're a good man, Harry, and I'm very fond of you, so yes please, I would like to marry you!' Harry swept Dolly up into his arms and kissed her full on the lips.

Until that moment there had just been a few times when he had kissed her on the cheek, now any doubts that she may have had about marrying him just disappeared into thin air. When Harry eventually released Dolly she was blushing and breathless. 'Oh Harry, you've taken my breath away!' And as Harry went to put his arms around her once more she twisted away out of his reach. 'No Harry, not now. What if the children come in?'

'Lord luv a duck, Doll, the family will be as pleased as we are to hear our news.'

Harry was right, all the family were pleased to hear of the forthcoming wedding, and especially Rosie who decided at once that she would be a flower girl.

Harry and Dolly had intended to have a quiet wedding with only the immediate family attending but on the day so many people wanted to wish them well, that in the end it was open house. Friends and family were coming and going all day long.

Dolly's parents were more than pleased with the marriage. They weren't able to attend but they did send a telegram of congratulations.

The family moved into a larger house in Manor Park a few miles outside London. Harry had to cycle further to work but he managed to cope, he was strong and his bike, although old, was very sturdy.

To Harry's delight, the new house had a large garden. He was able to grow a lot more than would have been possible in the yard of the old house. Dolly had flowers to pick and the rooms were soon full of the colour and scent of them. It reminded her of the pretty garden that her father kept.

In the next few years there were a few additions to the family. First a tiny girl weighing just four pounds was born. Everyone including the doctors said that she wouldn't make it to her first year. She proved them all wrong; she was named Jessie, after Dolly's mother. Then came a bonny little boy with large dark-brown eyes and lots of curls. this was Arthur; he was a charmer and everyone that met him fell under his spell.

Rosie was in her element. She had a new mother, a new brother and two new sisters as well. This meant of course that she was no longer the youngest in the family. Rosie loved playing mother with the new babies; she would wheel them about in the pram for hours. Ivy would be holding on to the pram handle, walking nicely beside her 'big sister'. Rosie liked that feeling of being one of the older children. She was very happy indeed.

One day Dolly answered the front door and came face to face with a policeman. He wanted her to go to the police station right away, but with two very small children in the house that was not possible, and she told him so. Later, when Harry came home from work and Rosie was able to see to the little ones both she and Harry made their way down to the police station. Neither of them had the slightest idea what it was about.

They were taken into the small room at the back of the station and there was Charlie, sitting with his head in his hands. The policeman said he had stolen a bundle of wood and was caught with it as he was leaving the yard. There was quite a heated argument. Charlie kept saying. 'Honest guv, I was gonna pay for it on Friday when I got me wages.' But that cut no ice with the foreman; he insisted that Charlie had meant to steal the wood. Harry stood by what the lad said, of course. He offered to pay there and then for the wood.

Dolly had grumbled about having no firewood. The fire was not easy to light with just rolled-up newspaper. Young Charlie must have heard her. She didn't think that it would lead to anything like this, and she felt sure it was all her fault.

The site manager insisted that it went to court. Harry told him that Charlie had never done anything like this before, that he was always honest.

'He's a good boy, Guv'ner, and he's a very hard worker. He never stays off work even when he's not feeling too good.'

Many of Charlie's workmates spoke up for him, but the foreman was new to that site. He said there had been trouble with boys stealing things at the other sites he had worked at and 'he wasn't going to put up with it happening here'.

Charlie had to go to court and after a very short trial he was found guilty of stealing wood from the yard. Harry, Dolly and the family were shocked when they were told that his punishment was going to be the 'Cat'.

The Cat o' Nine Tails was a particularly nasty punishment. Charlie was flogged with a whip with nine ends to it; he was unwell for a long time afterwards.

It was a terrible time for the family and the only reason they got through it was because they were so close. They never stopped believing in Charlie's innocence. They knew that if he said he was going to pay for the wood then that is what he would have done. This unjust punishment changed Charlie. When the wounds had healed, he decided to join the Army. Harry didn't try to talk him out of it; in fact, he thought it was probably for the best. Perhaps, when Charlie got away from the area where everyone knew what had happened, he would feel better.

Charlie had only been in the Army for a few months when he was sent to Egypt. He took to the Army like a duck to water and his letters were full of news about his new life. He enjoyed the life so much that he signed on for another five years.

Chapter 26

There was a strange silence about the house after Charlie left. It was a long time before things got back to normal, or as normal as they could be with Charlie gone away.

Once again money was getting tight. Harry couldn't always afford to buy leather to mend the children's shoes; they often had to have cardboard put inside to cover up the holes and help keep the cold out. Harry would cut the cardboard to shape and say. 'Don't worry, duck, when my boat comes home I'll buy us all some new shoes.' Inside, his heart was breaking.

Dolly found a few little jobs so as to bring more money into the house. For a while, she looked after other people's children whilst their mothers went out to work, she also did washing for a family along the road. When those jobs came to an end she found a small cleaning job in the local school. It was only two hours a day but it did bring in a little money.

The next upset was to do with Billy. Unlike his brothers, he was work-shy: every time he managed to find work it seemed to last only for a week at most. He was always sacked, mostly for skiving off, but sometimes just because when he *was* there he didn't work. Billy took to doing odd jobs; he worked at the fairground and on the boating lake. He worked on the barges for a while and sometimes he helped the local coalman. He never had a regular job and was always short of money. Dolly took pity on him and used to give him a few shillings now and again, but then Harry found out and said she wasn't to do it any more.

'You don't go out to work to keep him in cigarettes. He's a lazy good-for-nothing! Let him earn his own money. Albert doesn't have any trouble keeping a job.'

Harry was right. Albert had kept the same job for about four years. He worked in a warehouse and was getting on very well there. He had never been without a job. Even when he left school at the age of fourteen he got himself a job selling a kind of iced lollipop called 'Fro Joys'. He would ride around the streets on a bicycle with a large icebox built on to the front, calling out to attract customers: *'Fro Joys! Fro Joys!'* Rosie and the other children loved it when he stopped outside the house; he would cut a sixpenny 'Fro Joy' in four to be shared between them. When they saw him in his white coat and smart hat with its red band round it, they were very proud to tell everyone they met that he was *their* brother.

When Rosie was old enough to go to work, Dolly said she should go into service and Rosie liked the idea. A neighbour gave them the address of a lady whom she knew was looking for a young girl to help with the housework. They wrote to ask for an appointment and a few days later they went off on the bus to meet with the lady in question.

Chapter 27

When the appointment day came around Dolly and Rosie took the bus to Stratford. The lady seemed very nice. It was a grand house that she lived in; Dolly and Rosie were quite in awe of the place.

Mrs Thornton, (that was her name), greeted them in a very friendly way and served them with tea and cakes. She said she thought Rosie should live in, as it would be too far for her to travel home every day.

'She will be able to go home on Saturday afternoon and stay till Sunday evening.'

Dolly hadn't expected that Rosie would be living away from home and wasn't too sure about letting her take the job, but Rosie herself was certain that it was what she wanted to do, so after some discussion it was decided that she would start on the following Monday, and would work a month to see how she got on with the work.

The wonderful Mrs Thornton turned out to be not so wonderful after all. Young Rosie found the work very hard; she was made to work from six in the morning till nine at night. After six months she had to leave. She left because the hard work and long hours were making her ill, but her employer insisted that it was because she was lazy and didn't do the work properly. Nothing could have been further from the truth.

Eventually, Rosie was brought back to perfect health and

went to work in the canteen of a factory where she was very happy and made lots of friends.

One day Harry received the news that Charlie was ill and was being sent home. As soon as he was notified of Charlie's arrival in the country Harry went to visit him in the London Hospital. He couldn't believe it was the same young man who had gone away. His face, although tanned, was drawn and his eyes looked like blue watery saucers. Harry was shocked to see how very thin he was. Charlie had fallen from a horse and damaged his back; he had also contracted dysentery during his stay in the hospital abroad. He was very ill. Later it was thought that he must have hit his head when he fell.

Charlie never recovered completely; he was like a different person. He spoke like a small child, repeating the same things over and over. He was also bedridden and never regained the use of his legs. He seemed happy enough, but it was very distressing for the family.

The younger children couldn't remember the 'Old Charlie' but they loved visiting him; he was obviously pleased to see them too, even though he didn't really know who they were. He enjoyed their company, even more than the rest of the family. Harry and Dolly grieved for him and the loss of his young life but nothing could be done. It was very sad indeed. When his general health improved Charlie was taken to an asylum where he spent the rest of his life.

Chapter 28

The newspapers were full of bad news, telling of the unrest in Europe. There were groups of men led by a man called Mosley; they were riding around London, shouting propaganda from the back of lorries. They were fascists and came to be known as the 'Black Shirts' because of the clothes they always wore. They were trying to turn the British against the Jews, saying that Britain should be only for the British. There were many Jewish people living in London and they began to fear for their lives. The British people and the government, however, would not put up with it and they put the leader of the Black Shirts in prison.

Harry was always going on about the Black Shirts, 'Why don't they leave us alone to live our lives in peace instead of going round stirring up trouble?' Albert wasn't happy about them either. He could still remember the last war even though he had been very young. He and Harry would sit up long after the others had gone to bed, talking about the possibility of war.

One day when Harry came home from work the children could see a large wooden box strapped to the carrier of his bicycle. Jessie and little Arthur clambered around trying to help undo the straps.

'Hold on! Hold on! Just a minute, Lord luv a duck! How do you expect me to undo the buckles when there are hands and fingers everywhere?'

The children reluctantly stepped back to let Harry lift the box from his bicycle and carry it through into the garden, but they weren't far behind when at last he rested it on the top of the coal bin. Slowly he opened the lid of the box and to the delight of the youngsters he lifted out a large white rabbit. There were whoops of joy and excitement. They were allowed to stroke and make a fuss of the animal until Harry had eaten his dinner, then they all set about making a hutch for the white rabbit to live in.

Over the next few months Harry brought two more rabbits home on the back of his bike, and of course the inevitable happened. Rabbit pie was often on the menu after that, but the large white one that had been Harry's first purchase became Jessie's pet and was named Snowy.

Jessie spent hours caring for Snowy. Every school day she would bring dandelions, picked on her way home, and every weekend she would clean out his hutch and give him fresh hay, 'to make his home beautiful' she said.

One day Jessie came home from school early. The class had been swimming and the children were told that they could go straight home instead of going back to the school.

It was the family custom to put their dirty clothing in the bottom of a cupboard in the kitchen, ready for the weekly wash, and this was the place that Jessie headed for. She had intended to throw her swimming things in with the washing but when she opened the door she was stopped in her tracks by what she saw there. Screaming, Jessie ran through into the garden dropping her swimming things as she went. When Albert came home from work he brought his bike along the back alley as usual so that he could put it in the garden shed, and found Jessie curled up in a ball fast asleep. He went to pick her up and saw that her face was tear-streaked and her eyes were red with crying. As Albert moved the child she woke up and began to cry again.

'What's the matter, Jess? Tell me what's upset you.'

Jessie stuttered through her tears. 'Dad's killed Snowy; he promised me he wouldn't.'

She had seen the dead rabbit hanging behind the cupboard door in the kitchen.

'Oh, Jess, he was getting old. I expect Dad thought he would be too tough to eat if he kept him much longer.'

Jessie looked up at Albert, the tears still streaming.

'But he was *my* rabbit, Dad gave him to *me*. I don't love Dad any more, I hate him! I hate him!'

Albert stayed with the little girl until she had calmed down then they both went into the house.

'Where have you been? I've been worried to death.' Dolly ran to Jessie and put her arms around her. 'What's the matter, love, why have you been crying? Has somebody hurt you?'

Albert explained the reason for Jessie's tears and Dolly tried to comfort her, but she just shed more tears.

It was a long time before that incident was forgotten. Indeed, Jessie never forgot it, but she did manage to put the memory to the back of her mind after a while. Harry brought home a beautiful angora rabbit for her to keep forever, but it wasn't the same and after a while she gave the new rabbit to Arthur.

Chapter 29

Dolly was expecting another baby and she hadn't been well for some time, and one day she was taken into hospital with pneumonia. Rosie took some time off work to look after the family. By this time Ivy was nearly eleven and Jessie was eight, little Arthur was just four. The two girls were attending school but the little boy hadn't yet started and had to be cared for at home.

Dolly was away for about two months and in that time she was very ill. Harry remembered how it had been for Lila and he was very worried for Dolly. She eventually rallied, but she was in and out of hospital until the birth of her baby, a little girl. The baby was born in June and was given that name. June was a pretty little thing with lots of fair curls; she was a very bonny baby in spite of the fact that her mother had been so ill just before her birth.

The country was still rumbling with the talk of war. Albert had fixed up a wireless set and every evening the family sat quietly listening to the news. Dolly and Rosie would be knitting, Ivy would be doing one of her jigsaw puzzles on the table and Jessie and Arthur would be in their den, hidden from view by the large dark cloth that covered the table. The only sound would be the clicking of the knitting needles and the voice of the newsreader as he gave out the latest news about the unrest in Europe.

The news was getting worse. Even the two young children under the table sensed that there was something wrong; they weren't quite sure what it was but sadly they were soon to find out.

The year was 1939.